Long Island Golf Connection
Covering Brooklyn. Queens. Nassau and Suffolk
UPDATED AND REVISED

Any comments, questions or suggestions
Call MJM Marketing
1 800 287-5017

Cover Designed By: Richard Long
Book Designed By: John Romano and Michael Dari
Cover Photo By: Jeannine Marie Ricciardi

We would like you to support our sponsors by visiting their stores and
using their services. Our book would not be if it were not for each one
of them.

MJM Marketing is pleased to offer a complete guide in the Long Island
Golf Connection. Information contained in this guide was provided by the
course itself and careful attention has been made to ensure accuracy and
detail. Such information is subject to change by the golf course and is not
guaranteed by MJM Marketing.

PUBLIC COURSES

Golf Tip

Aim for Success

Two of the most neglected basics in the game of golf are aim and set-up. Aim and set-up describe the alignment to a desired target, and the body's positions before starting a swing. The main problem I find has to do with people's natural desire to align their feet, knees, hips, chest and shoulders - rather than the ball - to the target. By positioning the body this way, a right handed player hitting a perfect shot will hit the ball to the right of the target, unless the ball is hooked.

If the body is lined up with the flag stick, this means that the ball is already 2 or 3 feet right of the target before it is even struck. That 2 or 3 foot error quickly becomes 10 to 20 yards by the time the ball travels 100 yards (and this is if the ball is hit perfectly straight). An incorrect set-up forces a golfer to do something abnormal with his/her swing to get the ball to draw or fade to the target.

Since the goal for most players is to hit a consistently straight ball, the key is to align the ball and clubface to the target. Now, miss hit shots to the left or right have a better chance of working out. The best way to see a problem with a person's aim and set-up is to stand directly behind them. They can then be directed into the proper position and practice until they get used to it. Another way to make people realize this principle is to have them putt a few balls. Ask them way they aim the ball and putter to the hole when they putt, but aim their body at the hole from the fairway. Explain that the club and the ball should always aim at the hole, whether the golfer is putting or hitting from the fairway.

Both low and high handicappers can benefit from a quick check of their alignment and they may just find that they hit more fairways and greens. The last thing we all need is to have a shot doomed before we even start the swing.

Play Golf, Don't Play Swing
Mastering the Mental Game
by Judy Anderson

If you are serious enough about golf to be reading this book, you probably have made a commitment to the game and have spent a lot of time and money on it. Still, if you're like the majority of amateur golfers, you don't play golf!

Sounds incredible, doesn't it? But if you're out on the course thinking about the mechanics of your swing and trying to fix your game, you're not playing golf. You're playing swing! The place to work on the swing is at the practice range. When you're on the course, you need to trust your swing so you're able to focus on playing golf. To do this you need a strong mental game.

Ask any pro and they'll tell you that the mental game is critically important. You can master the swing, have the best equipment, and be in great physical shape. But unless you have strong mental game skills, you're not playing well consistently. Some pros on the Senior Tour who learned the game without the benefit of a lot of lessons on the mechanics of the swing will tell you that the game is 90% mental!! Course conditions vary and your physical game will fluctuate. So the pros who are consistently in the money have learned to focus on their mental game.

Amateurs usually try to improve their game by working on their swing or buying new equipment. Most totally neglect the mental game. Those who have tried to work on it often find it difficult to master. That's because although books have been written on the mental game, most of the information has been very generic and based on principles developed through research on other sports. It's the equivalent of giving everyone the same set of clubs, regardless of their physical requirements or individual swing. And then sending them out to play not knowing which club to use for which shot.

Finally someone has simplified the mental game. Dr. Deborah Graham is the first psychologist to study the champions on the LPGA, PGA, and the Senior PGA Tours. She learned that eight specific personality traits set the champions apart from the pros who win only occasionally. She found that the eight traits make up a Champion profile. And everyone's profile is different. This means that your personality influences who you are on the golf course. Your mental game is as individual as your swing! No wonder the generic mental techniques have been so difficult for most golfers to apply.

The eight Champion traits from the basis of the GolfPsych system. Knowing how you rate on the eight traits and then learning mental game techniques selected specifically for you will allow you to master the following skills, just the way the Champion pros have.

The 5 Components of the Mental Game

1. Concentration and focus. This is the ability to focus on what's necessary to successfully execute the shot. When you can't concentrate, your focus widens and you can become distracted by other players, adverse course conditions, and even your own thoughts. This focus cannot bo on your swing mechanics. That only gets you into the mode of "playing swing" rather than golf.

2. Thought control. Regulating your thoughts between shots and before the round is a critical skill to master. Thinking the wrong thoughts can stimulate your emotions, which makes it even more difficult to concentrate and focus. This may explain what happens to you when you play well on the front nine but totally lose it after the turn.

3. Managing Tension. Your mental game will suffer unless you can stay relaxed throughout the round. And it isn't just the negative emotions! Even getting excited about a great shot can make it difficult to concentrate and can cause you to lose focus. Deep breathing is one of the best things you can do to regulate your tension level.

4. Confidence. A strong mental game require both personal and performance confidence. You have to feel comfortable with your physical skills in practice before you ever take your game out on the course. Keeping records will help you recognize areas that need improvement. Then you can work on increasing your performance confidence through goal oriented practice.

5. Mental preparation, imagery, and attitude. Many golfers will prepare for a round by warming up and practicing the mechanics. Very few will prepare mentally for the round. Make sure to take a short mental break before you start the round. This allows you to let go of any tensions and concerns you brought to the course with you. Without this mental break, it will be difficult to concentrate and stay focused as you begin to play. And, if time allows, practice your mental game on the driving range and at the practice green just before starting your round.

Your level of skill in these 5 areas of the mental game is based on how close your personality is to the 8 champion personality traits and how well you've learned how to think like a champion. None of the pros Dr. Graham tested were in the champion range on all 8 traits! Golf is a tough game and nobody's Perfect! But the pros have learned how to adapt their behavior to make them consistent winners.

Keep these 5 components of the mental game in mind as you progress through your round. Practice deep breathing to manage your tension. Control negative thinking about bad shots. Develop a pre-shot mental routine to help you focus. Start devoting just a little time to your mental game and you can make '98 your best season ever!!

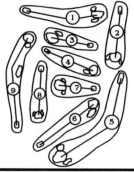

BAY PARK GC   (PUBLIC)

East Rockaway,NY

GOLF COURSE 516 571-7244

Course

HOLES	YARDS blue\white\red	PAR	RATING blue\white\red	SLOPE blue\white\red
9	0000\1956\0000	30	00.0\00.0\00.0	000\000\000

HOLES	1	2	3	4	5	6	7	8	9	TOTAL
PAR	4	3	3	3	4	3	3	3	4	30
YARDS	299	142	163	190	352	190	130	159	331	1956
(Blue)	000	000	000	000	000	000	000	000	000	0000

HOLES	10	11	12	13	14	15	16	17	18	TOTAL
PAR	0	0	0	0	0	0	0	0	0	00
YARDS	000	000	000	000	000	000	000	000	000	0000
(Blue)	000	000	000	000	000	000	000	000	000	0000

GREEN FEES:$8 on weekdays,$9 weekends.**First Tee Off:**Dawn.**Tee Times:**First come,
(Residents)   first serve.Course is closed on Wednesdays.

GREEN FEES:$16 on weekdays,$18 on weekends.
(Non-resident)

ARCHITECT:N\A
YEAR BUILT:1968
PRO: None
SEASON: March-December

DISCOUNTS: Seniors,Handicap,Volunteer
Firefighters
CART FEES: Pull carts $2.
SPIKE POLICY: Spikes or soft spikes
AVAILABLE FOR TOURNAMENTS:yes
CONTACT: Peggy Van Nostrand 516 571-7243.

COURSE DESCRIPTION:9 hole executive course with a few hills.

FEATURES\FACILITIES:

DRIVING RANGE-no
RESTAURANT-no
LOUNGE-yes
LESSONS-no
PRO SHOP-no

BANQUET-no
WOMEN'S LOCKERS-no
MEN'S LOCKERS-no
MEETING ROOM-no
NEARBY LODGING-no

PRACTICE AREA-yes
BAR-no
RENTAL CLUBS-no
CREDIT CARDS-no
SNACK BAR-no

DIRECTIONS: Southern State Parkway to exit 17 south (Ocean Ave).Stay on Ocean Ave
for approx. 3 miles and follow signs to course.

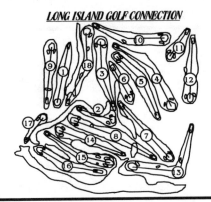

BERGEN POINT GC (PUBLIC)
West Babylon,NY

GOLF COURSE 516 661-8282
TEE TIMES 516 224-7275

Course

HOLES	YARDS blue\white\red	PAR	RATING blue\white\red	SLOPE blue\white\red
18	6576\6206\5729	71	71.4\69.2\71.8	121\118\116

HOLES	1	2	3	4	5	6	7	8	9	TOTAL
PAR	4	3	4	5	4	3	4	5	4	36
YARDS	332	173	395	490	397	185	389	497	327	3185
(Blue)	348	193	405	513	419	232	404	516	352	3382

HOLES	10	11	12	13	14	15	16	17	18	TOTAL
PAR	4	3	4	5	4	4	4	3	4	35
YARDS	404	155	334	464	380	367	358	143	416	3021
(Blue)	418	167	350	481	404	383	383	172	436	3194

GREEN FEES:$19 on weekdays,$20 weekends,with a Green Key Card.**First Tee Off:**7am
(Residents) \6am.**Tee Times:**You must be a Suffolk County resident with a Green Key
Card.Card holders can call 7 days in advance or day before from a touch
tone phone.There is a $3 reservation fee per golfer.

GREEN FEES:$28 on weekdays,$32 on weekends.**Tee Times:**Non-residents can not call
(Non-resident) for reservations.They must walk on.

ARCHITECT: Bill Mitchell
YEAR BUILT:1962
PRO: Victor Romano,PGA
SEASON: April-Mid December

DISCOUNTS: Seniors and Juniors
CART FEES:$25,Pull Carts $3
SPIKE POLICY: Soft spikes required
AVAILABLE FOR TOURNAMENTS: yes
CONTACT: Victor Romano **DAYS:**Wed-Fri (after 12pm)
Rotation start min 12-max 60.Shotgun start Mondays
only (125 players).

COURSE DESCRIPTION: Well bunkered links-style course.Water comes into play on 13
holes.Fair test of golf.

FEATURES\FACILITIES:

DRIVING RANGE-yes
RESTAURANT-yes
LOUNGE-yes
LESSONS-yes
PRO SHOP-yes

BANQUET-yes
WOMEN'S LOCKERS-yes
MEN'S LOCKERS-yes
MEETING ROOM-no
NEARBY LODGING-yes

PRACTICE AREA-yes
BAR-yes
RENTAL CLUBS-yes
CREDIT CARDS-yes
SNACK BAR-yes

DIRECTIONS: Southern State Parkway to Route 109 East.Proceed to Great East Neck Rd,
which turns into Bergen Ave.Continue to course.

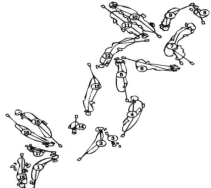

BETHPAGE STATE PARK

Farmingdale,NY   (PUBLIC)

Black Course

GOLF COURSE 516 249-0700
TEE TIMES 516 249-0707

HOLES	YARDS blue\white\red	PAR	RATING blue\white\red	SLOPE blue\white\red
18	7065\6556\6556	71	75.4\73.1\78.9	144\140\146

HOLES	1	2	3	4	5	6	7	8	9	TOTAL
PAR	4	4	3	5	4	4	5	3	4	36
YARDS	423	359	143	481	424	391	514	182	391	3308
(Blue)	430	371	160	528	446	404	585	195	401	3520

HOLES	10	11	12	13	14	15	16	17	18	TOTAL
PAR	4	4	4	5	3	4	4	3	4	35
YARDS	387	419	411	497	149	412	436	183	354	3248
(Blue)	419	433	480	572	159	438	466	200	378	3545

GREEN FEES:$25 on weekdays,$30 weekends.**First Tee Off:**Dawn.**Tee Times:**Call 7 days in advance with a photo ID card.Cards can be purchased at Bethpage, Montauk or Sunken Meadow.The card cost $20 and is valid for 3 years. There is a $3 reservation fee per golfer.

ARCHITECT:A.W. Tillinghast
YEAR BUILT:1935
PRO: Dick Smith,PGA
SEASON: All year

DISCOUNTS: Seniors and Twilight
CART FEES: No Carts,must walk
SPIKE POLICY: Spikes and Soft spikes
AVAILABLE FOR TOURNAMENTS:yes
CONTACT: Jim Larsen **DAYS:**Rotation start Mon, Fri. min 24-max 99.Shotgun start Tues,Wed,Thur 100 -144 players.

COURSE DESCRIPTION: The Black course has been chosen to host the US OPEN in 2002. With it's elevated tees,tremendous fairway bunkers,small greens and 4 inch rough,this course has been rated one of the best courses in the country.This course is for mid to low handicappers and might be difficult for the average golfer.

FEATURES\FACILITIES:
DRIVING RANGE-yes
RESTAURANT-yes
LOUNGE-yes
LESSONS-yes
PRO SHOP-yes

BANQUET-yes
WOMEN'S LOCKERS-yes
MEN'S LOCKERS-yes
MEETING ROOM-yes
NEARBY LODGING-yes

PRACTICE AREA-yes
BAR-yes
RENTAL CLUBS-yes
CREDIT CARDS-yes
SNACK BAR-yes

DIRECTIONS:495 LIE to exit 44 South and follow signs to Park and Golf Course.

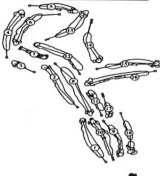

BETHPAGE STATE PARK

Farmingdale,NY   (PUBLIC)

Blue Course

GOLF COURSE 516 249-0700
TEE TIMES 516 249-0707

HOLES	YARDS blue\white\red	PAR	RATING blue\white\red	SLOPE blue\white\red
18	6684\6513\6213	72	72.2\71.4\75.5	126\124\130

HOLES	1	2	3	4	5	6	7	8	9	TOTAL
PAR	4	4	3	5	4	4	3	5	4	36
YARDS	421	446	180	480	303	465	180	547	336	3358
(Blue)	437	454	190	491	307	477	186	555	346	3443

HOLES	10	11	12	13	14	15	16	17	18	TOTAL
PAR	4	3	5	4	4	4	5	3	4	36
YARDS	378	183	471	366	362	379	494	165	357	3155
(Blue)	388	191	481	374	368	391	504	175	369	3241

GREEN FEES:$20 on weekdays,$24 weekends.**First Tee Off:**Dawn.**Tee Times:**Call 7
days in advance with a photo ID card.Cards can be purchased at Bethpage,
Montauk or Sunken Meadow.The card cost $20 and is valid for 3 years.
There is a $3 reservation fee per golfer.

ARCHITECT: Alfred Tull
YEAR BUILT:1958
PRO: Dick Smith,PGA
SEASON: All year

DISCOUNTS: Seniors and Twilight
CART FEES:$25,pull carts $1.50
SPIKE POLICY: Spikes and Soft spikes
AVAILABLE FOR TOURNAMENTS:yes
CONTACT: Jim Larsen **DAYS:**Rotation start Mon,
Fri. min 24-max 99.Shotgun start Tues,Wed,Thur
100 -144 players.

COURSE DESCRIPTION: Small greens,elevated tees,well-bunkered course with many
hills.

FEATURES\FACILITIES:
DRIVING RANGE-yes
RESTAURANT-yes
LOUNGE-yes
LESSONS-yes
PRO SHOP-yes

BANQUET-yes
WOMEN'S LOCKERS-yes
MEN'S LOCKERS-yes
MEETING ROOM-yes
NEARBY LODGING-yes

PRACTICE AREA-yes
BAR-yes
RENTAL CLUBS-yes
CREDIT CARDS-yes
SNACK BAR-yes

DIRECTIONS: 495 LIE to exit 44 South and follow signs to Park and Golf Course.

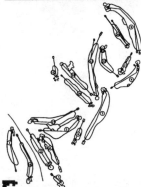

BETHPAGE STATE PARK
Farmingdale,NY   (PUBLIC)

Green Course

GOLF COURSE 516 249-0700
TEE TIMES 516 249-0707

HOLES	YARDS blue\white\red	PAR	RATING blue\white\red	SLOPE blue\white\red
18	0000\6267\5903	71	00.0\69.8\73.3	000\121\125

HOLES	1	2	3	4	5	6	7	8	9	TOTAL
PAR	4	4	3	4	4	3	5	4	5	36
YARDS	342	374	145	357	385	183	498	349	554	3187
(Red)	334	360	123	339	371	169	484	337	526	3043

HOLES	10	11	12	13	14	15	16	17	18	TOTAL
PAR	4	3	4	5	4	3	4	4	4	35
YARDS	339	168	289	572	349	199	355	414	395	3080
(Red)	295	156	269	522	339	165	341	404	369	2860

GREEN FEES:$20 on weekdays,$24 weekends.**First Tee Off:**Dawn.**Tee Times:**Call 7 days in advance with a photo ID card.Cards can be purchased at Bethpage, Montauk or Sunken Meadow.The card cost $20 and is valid for 3 years. There is a $3 reservation fee per golfer.

ARCHITECT:A.W Tillinghast
YEAR BUILT:1935
PRO: Dick Smith,PGA
SEASON: All year

DISCOUNTS: Seniors and Twilight
CART FEES: No Carts,must walk
SPIKE POLICY: Spikes and Soft spikes
AVAILABLE FOR TOURNAMENTS:yes
CONTACT: Jim Larsen **DAYS:**Rotation start Mon, Fri. min 24-max 99.Shotgun start Tues,Wed,Thur 100 -144 players.

COURSE DESCRIPTION: Small greens,elevated tees,well-bunkered course with many hills.This like the Black,you must walk.No carts.

FEATURES\FACILITIES:

DRIVING RANGE-yes
RESTAURANT-yes
LOUNGE-yes
LESSONS-yes
PRO SHOP-yes

BANQUET-yes
WOMEN'S LOCKERS-yes
MEN'S LOCKERS-yes
MEETING ROOM-yes
NEARBY LODGING-yes

PRACTICE AREA-yes
BAR-yes
RENTAL CLUBS-yes
CREDIT CARDS-yes
SNACK BAR-yes

DIRECTIONS:495 LIE to exit 44 South and follow signs to Park and Golf Course.

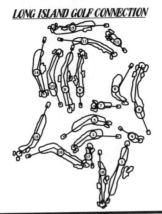

BETHPAGE STATE PARK

Farmingdale,NY   (PUBLIC)

Red Course

GOLF COURSE 516 249-0700
TEE TIMES 516 249-0707

HOLES	YARDS blue\white\red	PAR	RATING blue\white\red	SLOPE blue\white\red
18	6756\6537\6198	70	73.0\72.0\76.0	127\125\131

HOLES	1	2	3	4	5	6	7	8	9	TOTAL
PAR	4	4	4	3	5	4	3	4	4	35
YARDS	464	392	368	161	510	338	174	366	452	3225
(Blue)	471	401	382	171	528	350	184	378	466	3331

HOLES	10	11	12	13	14	15	16	17	18	TOTAL
PAR	4	4	3	4	4	4	5	3	4	35
YARDS	402	418	179	386	421	438	521	160	387	3312
(Blue)	416	432	189	400	435	452	535	165	401	3425

GREEN FEES:$20 on weekdays,$24 weekends.**First Tee Off:**Dawn.**Tee Times:**Call 7 days in advance with a photo ID card.Cards can be purchased at Bethpage, Montauk or Sunken Meadow.The card cost $20 and is valid for 3 years. There is a $3 reservation fee per golfer.

ARCHITECT:A.W. Tillinghast
YEAR BUILT:1935
PRO: Dick Smith,PGA
SEASON: All year

DISCOUNTS: Seniors and Twilight
CART FEES:$25,Pull carts $1.50
SPIKE POLICY: Spikes and Soft spikes
AVAILABLE FOR TOURNAMENTS:yes
CONTACT: Jim Larsen **DAYS:**Rotation start Mon, Fri. min 24-max 99.Shotgun start Tues,Wed,Thur 100 -144 players.

COURSE DESCRIPTION: Long par 4's,elevated tees,and well-bunkered.

FEATURES\FACILITIES:
DRIVING RANGE-yes
RESTAURANT-yes
LOUNGE-yes
LESSONS-yes
PRO SHOP-yes

BANQUET-yes
WOMEN'S LOCKERS-yes
MEN'S LOCKERS-yes
MEETING ROOM-yes
NEARBY LODGING-yes

PRACTICE AREA-yes
BAR-yes
RENTAL CLUBS-yes
CREDIT CARDS-yes
SNACK BAR-yes

DIRECTIONS:495 LIE to exit 44 South and follow signs to Park and Golf Course.

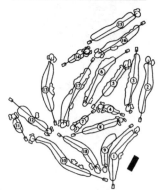

BETHPAGE STATE PARK
Farmingdale,NY   (PUBLIC)
Yellow Course

GOLF COURSE 516 249-0700
TEE TIMES 516 249-0707

HOLES	YARDS blue\white\red	PAR	RATING blue\white\red	SLOPE blue\white\red
18	6316\6171\5966	71	70.1\69.5\75.0	121\120\128

HOLES	1	2	3	4	5	6	7	8	9	TOTAL
PAR	4	4	4	3	4	5	3	4	4	35
YARDS	422	400	408	160	341	489	173	341	323	3057
(Blue)	434	404	419	170	350	494	177	346	332	3126

HOLES	10	11	12	13	14	15	16	17	18	TOTAL
PAR	5	3	4	4	3	4	4	5	4	36
YARDS	534	180	276	429	185	361	300	492	357	3114
(Blue)	547	190	277	446	191	370	305	495	369	3190

GREEN FEES:$20 on weekdays,$24 weekends.**First Tee Off:**Dawn.**Tee Times:**Call 7 days in advance with a photo ID card.Cards can be purchased at Bethpage, Montauk or Sunken Meadow.The card cost $20 and is valid for 3 years. There is a $3 reservation fee per golfer.

ARCHITECT: Alfred Tull
YEAR BUILT:1958
PRO: Dick Smith,PGA
SEASON: All year

DISCOUNTS: Seniors and Twilight
CART FEES:$25,Pull carts $1.50
SPIKE POLICY: Spikes and Soft spikes
AVAILABLE FOR TOURNAMENTS:yes
CONTACT: Jim Larsen **DAYS:**Rotation start Mon, Fri. min 24-max 99.Shotgun start Tues,Wed,Thur 100 -144 players.

COURSE DESCRIPTION: Well-bunkered,yet easiest of all Bethpage courses.

FEATURES\FACILITIES:
DRIVING RANGE-yes
RESTAURANT-yes
LOUNGE-yes
LESSONS-yes
PRO SHOP-yes

BANQUET-yes
WOMEN'S LOCKERS-yes
MEN'S LOCKERS-yes
MEETING ROOM-yes
NEARBY LODGING-yes

PRACTICE AREA-yes
BAR-yes
RENTAL CLUBS-yes
CREDIT CARDS-yes
SNACK BAR-yes

DIRECTIONS:495 LIE to exit 44 South and follow signs to Park and Golf Course.

NO LAYOUT AVAILABLE

BREEZY POINT GC (PUBLIC)
Queens,NY

GOLF COURSE 718 474-1623

Pitch and Putt

HOLES	YARDS blue\white\red	PAR	RATING blue\white\red	SLOPE blue\white\red
18	0000\1696\0000	55	00.0\00.0\00.0	000\000\000

HOLES	1	2	3	4	5	6	7	8	9	TOTAL
PAR	3	3	3	3	3	3	3	3	3	27
YARDS	67	58	102	103	60	87	93	112	89	771
(Blue)	000	000	000	000	000	000	000	000	000	0000

HOLES	10	11	12	13	14	15	16	17	18	TOTAL
PAR	3	4	3	3	3	3	3	3	3	28
YARDS	90	150	80	89	112	97	140	80	87	925
(Blue)	000	000	000	000	000	000	000	000	000	0000

GREEN FEES:$8 on weekdays,$11 weekends.**First Tee Off:**7:30am.**Tee Times:**First come, first serve.

ARCHITECT:N\A
YEAR BUILT:N\A
PRO: None
SEASON: March- December

DISCOUNTS: Seniors
CART FEES: No carts
SPIKE POLICY: Spikes or soft spikes
AVAILABLE FOR TOURNAMENTS:no

COURSE DESCRIPTION:18 hole pitch and putt course.Wide open with some trees;no water holes.

FEATURES\FACILITIES:

DRIVING RANGE-no
RESTAURANT-no
LOUNGE-no
LESSONS-no
PRO SHOP-no

BANQUET-no
WOMEN'S LOCKERS-no
MEN'S LOCKERS-no
MEETING ROOM-no
NEARBY LODGING-no

PRACTICE AREA-yes
BAR-no
RENTAL CLUBS-yes
CREDIT CARDS-no
SNACK BAR-no

DIRECTIONS: Belt Parkway to exit 11S.Proceed on Flatbush Ave and go over bridge. Bear left and follow signs to Riis Park.

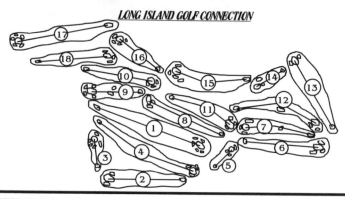

BRENTWOOD CC (PUBLIC)
Brentwood,NY

GOLF COURSE 516 436-6060
TEE TIMES 516 224-5648

Course

HOLES	YARDS blue\white\red	PAR	RATING blue\white\red	SLOPE blue\white\red
18	6173\5835\5093	72	69.3\67.8\68.4	121\118\111

HOLES	1	2	3	4	5	6	7	8	9	TOTAL
PAR	5	4	3	5	3	4	4	4	4	36
YARDS	480	352	169	483	133	375	350	285	303	2930
(Blue)	489	372	180	497	149	386	369	304	338	3084

HOLES	10	11	12	13	14	15	16	17	18	TOTAL
PAR	4	4	4	4	3	4	4	5	4	36
YARDS	308	284	370	297	158	404	262	467	355	2905
(Blue)	357	310	386	326	170	417	277	479	367	3089

GREEN FEES:$18 on weekdays,$20 on weekends.**First Tee Off:**6am.**Tee Times:**On
(Residents)　weekends and holidays you need tee time.Call on Tuesday prior.

GREEN FEES:$23 on weekdays,$28 on weekends.**Tee Times:**Non-residents can buy
(Non-resident)　pass for $10 to make reservations for weekends and holidays.Pass is
good for the season.

ARCHITECT: Devereux Emmet
YEAR BUILT:1925
PRO: Richie Loughlin,PGA
SEASON: March-December

DISCOUNTS: Seniors,and Juniors
CART FEES:$25,Pull carts $3
SPIKE POLICY: Soft spikes required
AVAILABLE FOR TOURNAMENTS:yes
CONTACT: Rich Loughlin **DAYS:**Mon-Fri,min 40
players.

COURSE DESCRIPTION: Tree-lined and flat.Good course for beginners and walkers.

FEATURES\FACILITIES:
DRIVING RANGE-no
RESTAURANT-yes
LOUNGE-yes
LESSONS-no
PRO SHOP-yes

BANQUET-yes
WOMEN'S LOCKERS-yes
MEN'S LOCKERS-yes
MEETING ROOM-yes
NEARBY LODGING-yes

PRACTICE AREA-yes
BAR-yes
RENTAL CLUBS-yes
CREDIT CARDS-yes
SNACK BAR-yes

DIRECTIONS: 495 LIE to exit 53. Cross Wicks Rd.to Washington Ave. Make a right.
Course is 1 mile on the left.

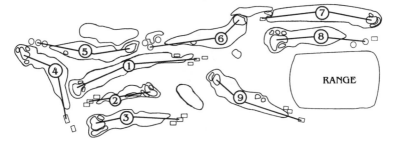

CALVERTON LINKS (PUBLIC)

Calverton,NY

GOLF COURSE 516 369-5200
TEE TIMES 516 369-5200

Course

HOLES	YARDS blue\white\red	PAR	RATING blue\white\red	SLOPE blue\white\red
9	3036\2682\2217	36	69.2\00.0\00.0	120\000\000

HOLES	1	2	3	4	5	6	7	8	9	TOTAL
PAR	5	3	4	4	4	4	5	4	3	36
YARDS	444	191	282	285	311	280	429	275	185	2682
(Blue)	507	222	315	321	341	310	444	338	238	3036

HOLES	10	11	12	13	14	15	16	17	18	TOTAL
PAR	0	0	0	0	0	0	0	0	0	00
YARDS	000	000	000	000	000	000	000	000	000	0000
(Blue)	000	000	000	000	000	000	000	000	000	0000

GREEN FEES:$14 on weekdays,$16 weekends for 9 holes.$24 on weekdays,$26 on weekends for 18 holes.**First Tee Off:**7am **Tee Times:**Call 7 days in advance at no extra charge.

ARCHITECT:N\A
YEAR BUILT:1993
PRO: Call for appt.
SEASON: All year

DISCOUNTS: None
CART FEES:$25 for 18,$13 for 9 holes
SPIKE POLICY: Soft spikes required
AVAILABLE FOR TOURNAMENTS:yes
CONTACT: John Shippers **DAYS:**Mon-Thurs. Start after 10am.

COURSE DESCRIPTION: Fairly simple layout,few water holes and elevated tees.

FEATURES\FACILITIES:

DRIVING RANGE-yes
RESTAURANT-no
LOUNGE-no
LESSONS-yes
PRO SHOP-yes

BANQUET-no
WOMEN'S LOCKERS-no
MEN'S LOCKERS-no
MEETING ROOM-no
NEARBY LODGING-yes

PRACTICE AREA-yes
BAR-beer only
RENTAL CLUBS-yes
CREDIT CARDS-yes
SNACK BAR-yes

DIRECTIONS:495 LIE to exit 71,Make left onto Edwards Ave.Go ½ mile course is on left.

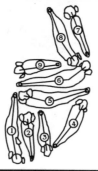

CANTIAGUE PARK GC (PUBLIC)
Hicksville,NY

GOLF COURSE 516 571-7061
TEE TIMES 516 571-7062

Executive Course

HOLES	YARDS blue\white\red	PAR	RATING blue\white\red	SLOPE blue\white\red
9	0000\1878\0000	30	00.0\00.0\00.0	000\000\000

HOLES	1	2	3	4	5	6	7	8	9	TOTAL
PAR	4	3	3	3	4	4	3	3	3	30
YARDS	259	173	150	200	257	272	157	228	182	1878
(Blue)	000	000	000	000	000	000	000	000	000	0000

HOLES	10	11	12	13	14	15	16	17	18	TOTAL
PAR	0	0	0	0	0	0	0	0	0	00
YARDS	000	000	000	000	000	000	000	000	000	0000
(Blue)	000	000	000	000	000	000	000	000	000	0000

GREEN FEES:$8 on weekdays,$9 weekends.**First Tee Off:**Dawn
(Resident)   Course is closed on Tuesday.

GREEN FEES:$16 on weekdays,$18 on weekends.
(Non-resident)

ARCHITECT:N\A
YEAR BUILT:1965
PRO: Keith Miller
SEASON: All year

DISCOUNTS: Seniors,Nassau Firefighters,
Handicapped
CART FEES: Pull carts $2.
SPIKE POLICY: Soft spikes required
AVAILABLE FOR TOURNAMENTS:no

COURSE DESCRIPTION: Open fairways,excellent for beginners.

FEATURES\FACILITIES:

DRIVING RANGE-yes
RESTAURANT-no
LOUNGE-no
LESSONS-yes
PRO SHOP-yes

BANQUET-no
WOMEN'S LOCKERS-no
MEN'S LOCKERS-no
MEETING ROOM-no
NEARBY LODGING-yes

PRACTICE AREA-yes
BAR-no
RENTAL CLUBS-yes
CREDIT CARDS-yes
SNACK BAR-yes

DIRECTIONS:495 LIE to exit 41 South,onto Route 106\107 South 1 mile to West John
St.Make a right.Course approx. ½ mile down on right.

NO LAYOUT AVAILABLE

CEDAR BEACH GC (PUBLIC)   GOLF COURSE 516 321-4562
Babylon,NY
Pitch and Putt

HOLES	YARDS blue\white\red	PAR	RATING blue\white\red	SLOPE blue\white\red
18	0000\1370\0000	54	00.0\00.0\00.0	000\000\000

HOLES	1	2	3	4	5	6	7	8	9	TOTAL
PAR	3	3	3	3	3	3	3	3	3	27
YARDS	65	80	90	55	60	70	65	90	70	645
(Blue)	000	000	000	000	000	000	000	000	000	0000

HOLES	10	11	12	13	14	15	16	17	18	TOTAL
PAR	3	3	3	3	3	3	3	3	3	27
YARDS	80	75	90	100	70	100	80	70	60	725
(Blue)	000	000	000	000	000	000	000	000	000	0000

GREEN FEES:$5 on weekdays,$5 weekends.**First Tee Off:**7am.**Tee Times:**First come, first serve.

ARCHITECT:N\A
YEAR BUILT:N\A
PRO: None
SEASON: All year

DISCOUNTS: Seniors
CART FEES: No carts
SPIKE POLICY: Spikes or soft spikes
AVAILABLE FOR TOURNAMENTS:no

COURSE DESCRIPTION: This is a pitch and putt course.Great for beginners,and to practice your short game.

FEATURES\FACILITIES:

DRIVING RANGE-no
RESTAURANT-no
LOUNGE-no
LESSONS-no
PRO SHOP-no

BANQUET-no
WOMEN'S LOCKERS-no
MEN'S LOCKERS-no
MEETING ROOM-no
NEARBY LODGING-no

PRACTICE AREA-yes
BAR-no
RENTAL CLUBS-yes
CREDIT CARDS-no
SNACK BAR-yes

DIRECTIONS: Northern State parkway to exit 33 (Wantagh Parkway).Proceed to Ocean Ave East.Course is on the right,after Jones Beach.

NO LAYOUT AVAILABLE

CEDARS GC   (PUBLIC)   GOLF COURSE 516 734-6363
Cutchogue,NY
Pitch and Putt

HOLES	YARDS blue\white\red	PAR	RATING blue\white\red	SLOPE blue\white\red
9	0000\1120\0000	27	00.0\00.0\00.0	000\000\000

HOLES	1	2	3	4	5	6	7	8	9	TOTAL
PAR	3	3	3	3	3	3	3	3	3	27
YARDS	130	110	120	115	125	175	100	120	125	1120
(Blue)	000	000	000	000	000	000	000	000	000	0000

HOLES	10	11	12	13	14	15	16	17	18	TOTAL
PAR	0	0	0	0	0	0	0	0	0	00
YARDS	000	000	000	000	000	000	000	000	000	0000
(Blue)	000	000	000	000	000	000	000	000	000	0000

GREEN FEES:$5.50 on weekdays,$7 weekends.**First Tee Off:**7:30am.**Tee Times:**First come,first serve.To play additional 9 holes $3 weekdays,$3.50 weekends.

ARCHITECT:N\A
YEAR BUILT:1964
PRO: Russell Case
SEASON: All year

DISCOUNTS: Seniors
CART FEES: Pull carts $1
SPIKE POLICY: Spikes or soft spikes
AVAILABLE FOR TOURNAMENTS:no

COURSE DESCRIPTION: This is a pitch and putt course.Great for beginners and to practice your short game.There is water on the 1st and 9th holes.

FEATURES\FACILITIES:
DRIVING RANGE-no
RESTAURANT-no
LOUNGE-no
LESSONS-yes
PRO SHOP-yes

BANQUET-no
WOMEN'S LOCKERS-no
MEN'S LOCKERS-no
MEETING ROOM-no
NEARBY LODGING-no

PRACTICE AREA-yes
BAR-no
RENTAL CLUBS-yes
CREDIT CARDS-no
SNACK BAR-no

DIRECTIONS:495 LIE to the last exit.Proceed East on Route 58 until it turns into Route 25.Proceed on Route 25 for 1 mile into Cutchogue.Make right onto Cases Lanes.Proceed ¼ mile to end and make a right to course.

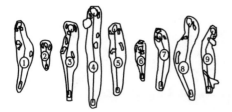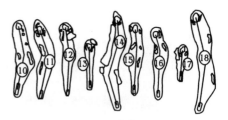

CHERRY CREEK GOLF LINKS
Riverhead,NY   (PUBLIC)

GOLF COURSE 516 369-8987
TEE TIMES 516 369-6500

Course

HOLES	YARDS blue\white\red	PAR	RATING blue\white\red	SLOPE blue\white\red
18	7187\6597\5756	73	73.8\71.1\72.1	127\121\122

HOLES	1	2	3	4	5	6	7	8	9	TOTAL
PAR	4	3	4	5	4	3	4	5	4	36
YARDS	402	130	411	585	386	163	313	495	371	3256
(Blue)	446	145	465	623	439	192	352	515	393	3570

HOLES	10	11	12	13	14	15	16	17	18	TOTAL
PAR	4	4	4	3	5	4	4	3	6	37
YARDS	405	370	389	184	521	357	349	154	612	3341
(Blue)	419	396	422	224	558	397	387	170	644	3617

GREEN FEES:$27 on weekdays,$32 on weekends.**First Tee Off:**6:30am.**Tee Times:**To reserve tee time you must join reservation club for an annual fee of $30. Members can call 5 days in advance.There is a $3 charge per player on weekdays and a $5 charge on weekends.

ARCHITECT: Young&Young
YEAR BUILT:1996
PRO: Steve Keating,PGA
SEASON: All year

DISCOUNTS: None
CART FEES:$26,Pull carts $5.00
SPIKE POLICY: Soft spikes optional
AVAILABLE FOR TOURNAMENTS:yes
CONTACT: Steve Keating **DAYS:**Mon-Fri min 20 players for rotation start.Shotgun min 130, holidays,weekends and Tuesdays not included.

COURSE DESCRIPTION: Flat links style course.Water comes into play on 8 holes.The 18th hole is a par 6 over 600 yards.

FEATURES\FACILITIES:

DRIVING RANGE-yes
RESTAURANT-yes
LOUNGE-yes
LESSONS-yes
PRO SHOP-yes

BANQUET-yes
WOMEN'S LOCKERS-no
MEN'S LOCKERS-yes
MEETING ROOM-no
NEARBY LODGING-no

PRACTICE AREA-yes
BAR-yes
RENTAL CLUBS-yes
CREDIT CARDS-yes
SNACK BAR-yes

DIRECTIONS:495 LIE to exit 73.Proceed on Route 58 East approx. 4 miles to traffic circle.Go ¾ around circle and head North on Roanoke Ave.Proceed 1 ½ miles to Reeves Ave and make a right.Course is ¾ mile on left.

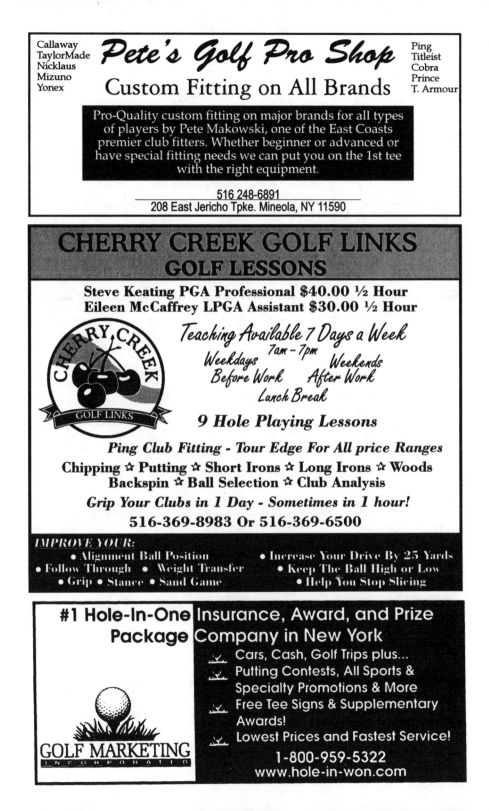

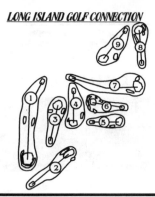

CHRISTOPHER MORLEY GC

North Hills,NY   (PUBLIC)

GOLF COURSE 516 571-8120

Course

HOLES	YARDS blue\white\red	PAR	RATING blue\white\red	SLOPE blue\white\red
9	0000\1520\0000	29	00.0\00.0\00.0	000\000\000

HOLES	1	2	3	4	5	6	7	8	9	TOTAL
PAR	4	3	3	3	3	3	4	3	3	29
YARDS	267	143	153	119	145	152	300	97	144	1520
(Blue)	000	000	000	000	000	000	000	000	000	0000

HOLES	10	11	12	13	14	15	16	17	18	TOTAL
PAR	0	0	0	0	0	0	0	0	0	00
YARDS	000	000	000	000	000	000	000	000	000	0000
(Blue)	000	000	000	000	000	000	000	000	000	0000

GREEN FEES:$8 on weekdays,$9 weekends.**First Tee Off:**Dawn.**Tee Times:**First come,
(Resident)   first serve.Residents must have leisure pass.Course is closed on Monday.

GREEN FEES:$16 on weekdays,$18 on weekends.
(Non-resident)

ARCHITECT:N\A
YEAR BUILT:N\A
PRO: None
SEASON: March-December

DISCOUNTS: Seniors,Handicap,Volunteer
Firefighters.With leisure pass.
CART FEES: Pull carts $2.
SPIKE POLICY: Soft spikes required
AVAILABLE FOR TOURNAMENTS:no

COURSE DESCRIPTION:9 hole executive course with a few hills.Excellent for beginners.

FEATURES\FACILITIES:

DRIVING RANGE-no
RESTAURANT-no
LOUNGE-no
LESSONS-no
PRO SHOP-no

BANQUET-no
WOMEN'S LOCKERS-no
MEN'S LOCKERS-no
MEETING ROOM-no
NEARBY LODGING-no

PRACTICE AREA-yes
BAR-no
RENTAL CLUBS-no
CREDIT CARDS-no
SNACK BAR-no

DIRECTIONS:495 LIE to exit 36.Proceed North on Searingtown Rd.Course is on the right.

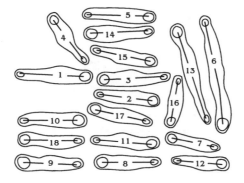

CLEARVIEW GC (PUBLIC)

Bayside,NY

Course

GOLF COURSE 718 229-2570

TEE TIMES 718 225-4653

HOLES	YARDS blue\white\red	PAR	RATING blue\white\red	SLOPE blue\white\red
18	0000\6283\5497	70	00.0\69.2\70.4	000\114\115

HOLES	1	2	3	4	5	6	7	8	9	TOTAL
PAR	4	5	4	3	4	4	3	4	4	35
YARDS	355	473	411	170	395	390	134	435	425	3188
(Blue)	000	000	000	000	000	000	000	000	000	0000

HOLES	10	11	12	13	14	15	16	17	18	TOTAL
PAR	4	4	3	4	4	5	3	4	4	35
YARDS	375	345	150	343	442	471	194	395	380	3095
(Blue)	000	000	000	000	000	000	000	000	000	0000

GREEN FEES:$18 on weekdays,$20 weekends.**First Tee Off:**Dawn.**Tee Times:**Call 10
(Resident)   days prior.There is a $2 reservation fee per golfer.

GREEN FEES:$24 on weekdays,$26 on weekends.
(Non-resident)

ARCHITECT:N\A
YEAR BUILT:N\A
PRO: Eric Chun,PGA
SEASON: All Year

DISCOUNTS: Seniors and Twilight
CART FEES:$24.50\$25.50
SPIKE POLICY: Soft spikes preferred
AVAILABLE FOR TOURNAMENTS:yes
CONTACT: Joanne Passutto **DAYS:**Mon-Sun
min 10-max 62.State restrictions apply.(call for
details).

COURSE DESCRIPTION: Fairly easy,yet deceiving course.Fairways are tree-lined and
wide.

FEATURES\FACILITIES:

DRIVING RANGE-no
RESTAURANT-yes
LOUNGE-yes
LESSONS-yes
PRO SHOP-yes

BANQUET-no
WOMEN'S LOCKERS-yes
MEN'S LOCKERS-yes
MEETING ROOM-no
NEARBY LODGING-yes

PRACTICE AREA-no
BAR-no
RENTAL CLUBS-yes
CREDIT CARDS-yes
SNACK BAR-yes

DIRECTIONS:495 LIE to Clearview Expressway North.Proceed to last exit before Throgs
Neck Bridge.Make a left off of ramp.Course is on the left.

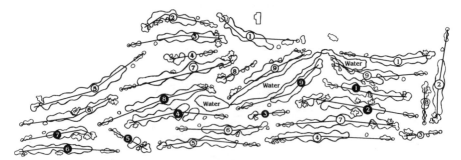

⑦ = Valley ❷ = Lake ① = Pines

COLONIAL SPRINGS GC

Farmingdale,NY　　(PUBLIC)

Lake\Pines

GOLF COURSE 516 643-0051

TEE TIMES 516 643-0051

HOLES	YARDS blue\white\red	PAR	RATING blue\white\red	SLOPE blue\white\red
18	6793\6404\5467	72	71.7\69.9\70.5	123\119\118

HOLES	1	2	3	4	5	6	7	8	9	TOTAL
PAR	4	5	3	4	3	4	4	5	4	36
YARDS	352	505	133	420	163	413	298	490	387	3161
(Blue)	366	525	159	440	181	435	316	517	420	3359

HOLES	10	11	12	13	14	15	16	17	18	TOTAL
PAR	4	4	3	5	4	4	5	3	4	36
YARDS	382	377	154	522	410	363	500	145	390	3243
(Blue)	395	405	171	545	430	386	530	162	410	3434

GREEN FEES:$56 Mon-Thurs,$62 Fri,$69 weekends and holidays,with reservation card. Reservation card is $25 for the season.Cart fees are included and mandatory.**First Tee Off:**6:30am.**Tee Times:**For Mon-Thurs call 7 days in advance,for Fri call 12pm the preceding Wed,for weekends call day before at 9am.

GREEN FEES:$62 Mon-Thurs,$69 Fri,$75 weekends and holidays,without reservation card.Cart fees are included and mandatory.**Tee Times:**See above.

ARCHITECT: Arthur Hills
YEAR BUILT:1994
PRO: Mike Wade,PGA
SEASON: April-November

DISCOUNTS: Twilight
CART FEES: Included
SPIKE POLICY: Soft spikes required
AVAILABLE FOR TOURNAMENTS:yes
CONTACT: Joe Williams **DAYS:**Mon&Tues
Mon min 120,Tues, min 12-max 56.

COURSE DESCRIPTION:27 holes of beautiful turf designed by Arthur Hills.5 of 27 holes are encompassed by an 11 acre lake.You will think you are in North Carolina.

FEATURES\FACILITIES:

DRIVING RANGE-yes
RESTAURANT-yes
LOUNGE-yes
LESSONS-yes
PRO SHOP-yes

BANQUET-yes
WOMEN'S LOCKERS-yes
MEN'S LOCKERS-yes
MEETING ROOM-no
NEARBY LODGING-no

PRACTICE AREA-yes
BAR-yes
RENTAL CLUBS-yes
CREDIT CARDS-yes
SNACK BAR-yes

DIRECTIONS:495 LIE to exit 49 South.Stay on the Service Rd to the third traffic light (Pinelawn Rd),make a right.Proceed 2 ½ miles and make a left directly over the RR tracks onto Long Island Ave.Course is ½ mile on the right.

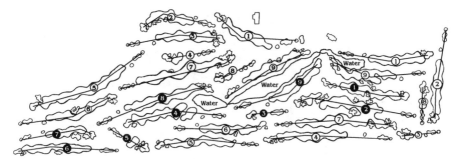

⑦ = Valley ❷ = Lake ① = Pines

COLONIAL SPRINGS GC

Farmingdale,NY (PUBLIC)

Lake\Valley

GOLF COURSE 516 643-0051

TEE TIMES 516 643-0051

HOLES	YARDS blue\white\red	PAR	RATING blue\white\red	SLOPE blue\white\red
18	6736\6351\5448	72	71.6\69.9\70.5	125\121\120

HOLES	1	2	3	4	5	6	7	8	9	TOTAL
PAR	4	5	3	4	3	4	4	5	4	36
YARDS	352	505	133	420	163	413	298	490	387	3161
(Blue)	366	525	159	440	181	435	316	517	420	3359

HOLES	10	11	12	13	14	15	16	17	18	TOTAL
PAR	4	4	4	3	5	4	5	3	4	36
YARDS	335	305	405	186	527	401	495	157	379	3190
(Blue)	370	330	420	210	550	422	510	172	393	3377

GREEN FEES:$56 Mon-Thurs,$62 Fri,$69 weekends and holidays,with reservation card. Reservation card is $25 for the season.Cart fees are included and mandatory.**First Tee Off:**6:30am.**Tee Times:**For Mon-Thurs call 7 days in advance,for Fri call 12pm the preceding Wed,for weekends call day before at 9am.

GREEN FEES:$62 Mon-Thurs,$69 Fri,$75 weekends and holidays,without reservation card.Cart fees are included and mandatory.**Tee Times:**See above.

ARCHITECT: Arthur Hills
YEAR BUILT:1994
PRO: Mike Wade,PGA
SEASON: April-November

DISCOUNTS: Twilight
CART FEES: Included
SPIKE POLICY: Soft spikes required
AVAILABLE FOR TOURNAMENTS:yes
CONTACT: Joe Williams **DAYS:**Mon&Tues
Mon min 120,Tues, min 12-max 56.

COURSE DESCRIPTION:27 holes of beautiful turf designed by Arthur Hills.5 of 27 holes are encompassed by an 11 acre lake.You will think you are in North Carolina.

FEATURES\FACILITIES:

DRIVING RANGE-yes
RESTAURANT-yes
LOUNGE-yes
LESSONS-yes
PRO SHOP-yes

BANQUET-yes
WOMEN'S LOCKERS-yes
MEN'S LOCKERS-yes
MEETING ROOM-no
NEARBY LODGING-no

PRACTICE AREA-yes
BAR-yes
RENTAL CLUBS-yes
CREDIT CARDS-yes
SNACK BAR-yes

DIRECTIONS:495 LIE to exit 49 South.Stay on the Service Rd to the third traffic light (Pinelawn Rd),make a right.Proceed 2 ½ miles and make a left directly over the RR tracks onto Long Island Ave.Course is ½ mile on the right.

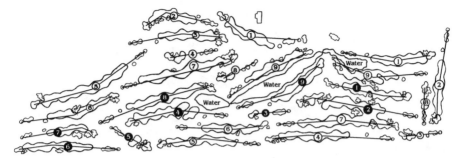

⑦ - Valley ❷ - Lake ① - Pines

COLONIAL SPRINGS GC

Farmingdale,NY   (PUBLIC)

Valley\Pines

GOLF COURSE 516 643-0051

TEE TIMES 516 643-0051

HOLES	YARDS blue\white\red	PAR	RATING blue\white\red	SLOPE blue\white\red
18	6811\6433\5485	72	70.8\70.0\70.4	124\120\119

HOLES	1	2	3	4	5	6	7	8	9	TOTAL
PAR	4	4	4	3	5	4	5	3	4	36
YARDS	335	305	405	186	527	401	495	157	379	3190
(Blue)	370	330	420	210	550	422	510	172	393	3377

HOLES	10	11	12	13	14	15	16	17	18	TOTAL
PAR	4	4	3	5	4	4	5	3	4	36
YARDS	382	377	154	522	410	363	500	145	390	3243
(Blue)	395	405	171	545	430	386	530	162	410	3434

GREEN FEES:$56 Mon-Thurs,$62 Fri,$69 weekends and holidays,with reservation card. Reservation card is $25 for the season.Cart fees are included and mandatory.**First Tee Off:**6:30am.**Tee Times:**For Mon-Thurs call 7 days in advance,for Fri call 12pm the preceding Wed,for weekends call day before at 9am.

GREEN FEES:$62 Mon-Thurs,$69 Fri,$75 weekends and holidays,without reservation card.Cart fees are included and mandatory.**Tee Times:**See above.

ARCHITECT: Arthur Hills
YEAR BUILT:1994
PRO: Mike Wade,PGA
SEASON: April-November

DISCOUNTS: Twilight
CART FEES: Included
SPIKE POLICY: Soft spikes required
AVAILABLE FOR TOURNAMENTS:yes
CONTACT: Joe Williams **DAYS:**Mon&Tues
Mon min 120,Tues,min 12-max 56.

COURSE DESCRIPTION:27 holes of beautiful turf designed by Arthur Hills.5 of 27 holes are encompassed by an 11 acre lake.You will think you are in North Carolina.

FEATURES\FACILITIES:

DRIVING RANGE-yes
RESTAURANT-yes
LOUNGE-yes
LESSONS-yes
PRO SHOP-yes

BANQUET-yes
WOMEN'S LOCKERS-yes
MEN'S LOCKERS-yes
MEETING ROOM-no
NEARBY LODGING-no

PRACTICE AREA-yes
BAR-yes
RENTAL CLUBS-yes
CREDIT CARDS-yes
SNACK BAR-yes

DIRECTIONS:495 LIE to exit 49 South.Stay on the Service Rd to the third traffic light (Pinelawn Rd),make a right.Proceed 2 ½ miles and make a left directly over the RR tracks onto Long Island Ave.Course is ½ mile on the right.

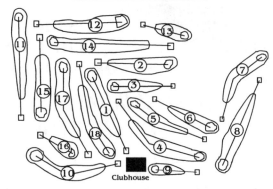

Clubhouse

CRAB MEADOW GC (Semi-Private)

Northport,NY

Course

GOLF COURSE 516 757-8800

TEE TIMES 516 757-2300

HOLES	YARDS blue\white\red	PAR	RATING blue\white\red	SLOPE blue\white\red
18	6613\6294\5845	72	70.9\69.7\72.6	118\116\120

HOLES	1	2	3	4	5	6	7	8	9	TOTAL
PAR	4	4	3	5	4	4	4	5	3	36
YARDS	367	378	205	482	373	322	345	457	150	3079
(Blue)	377	385	222	511	395	330	359	488	166	3233

HOLES	10	11	12	13	14	15	16	17	18	TOTAL
PAR	4	5	4	3	5	4	3	4	4	36
YARDS	358	458	417	175	512	358	127	403	407	3215
(Blue)	369	470	427	184	528	404	155	421	422	3380

GREEN FEES:$17 on weekdays,$17 weekends.**First Tee Off:**6:00am.**Tee Times:**You
(Resident) must be a Huntington Town Resident with a Course permit card.Cards
are $15 for the season.Call 7 days in advance or day before.There is a
$2.25 per golfer charge.

GREEN FEES:$30 on weekdays,$30 on weekends.**First Tee Off:**After 1:00pm,unless
(Non-resident) accompanied by a Town resident.

ARCHITECT: Bill Mitchell
YEAR BUILT:1965
PRO: Sal Silverstrone,PGA
SEASON: February-December

DISCOUNTS: Seniors and Twilight
CART FEES:$27
SPIKE POLICY: Spikes or soft spikes
AVAILABLE FOR TOURNAMENTS:yes
CONTACT: Gina 516 351-3097 **DAYS:**Monday
only,min 72 golfers.

COURSE DESCRIPTION: Trees and water provide challenging spots throughout the
course.

FEATURES\FACILITIES:

DRIVING RANGE-yes
RESTAURANT-yes
LOUNGE-yes
LESSONS-yes
PRO SHOP-yes

BANQUET-yes
WOMEN'S LOCKERS-yes
MEN'S LOCKERS-yes
MEETING ROOM-no
NEARBY LODGING-no

PRACTICE AREA-yes
BAR-yes
RENTAL CLUBS-yes
CREDIT CARDS-yes
SNACK BAR-yes

DIRECTIONS:495 LIE to exit 53 North (Sunken Meadow State Parkway),exit at 25A West.
Proceed approx 3 miles to Waterside Ave.Make a right,proceed for 2 miles.After bend bear
right and follow signs to course.

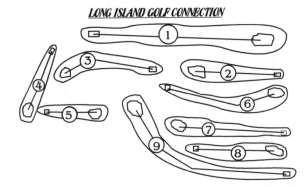

DIX HILLS CC (PUBLIC)

Dix Hills,NY

GOLF COURSE 516 271-4788

Executive Course

HOLES	YARDS blue\white\red	PAR	RATING blue\white\red	SLOPE blue\white\red
9	0000\2574\0000	35	00.0\00.0\00.0	000\000\000

HOLES	1	2	3	4	5	6	7	8	9	TOTAL
PAR	5	4	4	3	3	4	4	3	5	35
YARDS	475	256	303	90	168	312	261	239	470	2574
(Blue)	000	000	000	000	000	000	000	000	000	0000

HOLES	10	11	12	13	14	15	16	17	18	TOTAL
PAR	0	0	0	0	0	0	0	0	0	00
YARDS	000	000	000	000	000	000	000	000	000	0000
(Blue)	000	000	000	000	000	000	000	000	000	0000

GREEN FEES:$13 on weekdays,$15 weekends.**First Tee Off:**Dawn.**Tee Times:**Made in person,7 days in advance.There is a $3 charge per golfer.

ARCHITECT:N\A
YEAR BUILT:1940's
PRO: Bill Lavin,PGA
SEASON: April-November

DISCOUNTS: Seniors $10 Mon-Fri
CART FEES: Pull carts $3
SPIKE POLICY: Spikes or soft spikes
AVAILABLE FOR TOURNAMENTS:yes
CONTACT: Mark **DAYS:**Mon-Sun,min 20-max 72.

COURSE DESCRIPTION: Flat 9 hole course.Good for intermediates.

FEATURES\FACILITIES:

DRIVING RANGE-no
RESTAURANT-no
LOUNGE-no
LESSONS-yes
PRO SHOP-yes

BANQUET-no
WOMEN'S LOCKERS-no
MEN'S LOCKERS-no
MEETING ROOM-no
NEARBY LODGING-yes

PRACTICE AREA-yes
BAR-yes
RENTAL CLUBS-yes
CREDIT CARDS-no
SNACK BAR-yes

DIRECTIONS:495 LIE to Exit 50,left onto Bagatelle Rd.Proceed to Half Hollow Rd and make a right to course.

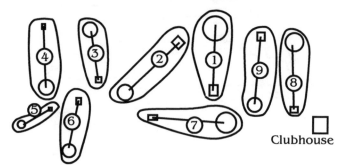

Clubhouse

DIX HILLS PARK GC (PUBLIC)

GOLF COURSE 516 499-8005

Dix Hills,NY

Executive Course

HOLES	YARDS blue\white\red	PAR	RATING blue\white\red	SLOPE blue\white\red
9	0000\1940\0000	31	00.0\00.0\00.0	000\000\000

HOLES	1	2	3	4	5	6	7	8	9	TOTAL
PAR	3	3	4	3	3	4	4	4	3	35
YARDS	166	130	275	140	121	265	312	283	248	1940
(Blue)	000	000	000	000	000	000	000	000	000	0000

HOLES	10	11	12	13	14	15	16	17	18	TOTAL
PAR	0	0	0	0	0	0	0	0	0	00
YARDS	000	000	000	000	000	000	000	000	000	0000
(Blue)	000	000	000	000	000	000	000	000	000	0000

GREEN FEES:$8 on weekdays,$9 weekends.**First Tee Off:**Dawn.**Tee Times:**First
(Residents)   come,first serve.Residents allowed 3 guests on weekdays,1 guest on
weekends.

GREEN FEES:$13 on weekdays,$15.50 on weekends.Must be accompanied by resident.
(Non-resident)

ARCHITECT: Edwin Voorhis   **DISCOUNTS:**Seniors (Town residents)
YEAR BUILT:1965   **CART FEES:**$14 per 9 holes.Pull carts $2 per.
PRO: Bob Greenstein,PGA   **SPIKE POLICY:**Spikes or Soft spikes
SEASON: All year   **AVAILABLE FOR TOURNAMENTS:**no

COURSE DESCRIPTION: Challenging tree-lined 9 hole course with narrow fairways.

FEATURES\FACILITIES:
DRIVING RANGE-yes   BANQUET-no   PRACTICE AREA-yes
RESTAURANT-no   WOMEN'S LOCKERS-no   BAR-no
LOUNGE-no   MEN'S LOCKERS-no   RENTAL CLUBS-yes
LESSONS-yes   MEETING ROOM-no   CREDIT CARDS-no
PRO SHOP-yes   NEARBY LODGING-yes   SNACK BAR-yes

DIRECTIONS:495 LIE to Exit 53 North to Vanderbuilt Parkway.Make a right to Course.

Family Golf Shop

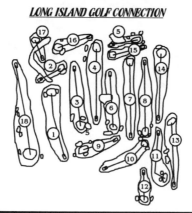

DOUGLASTON GC (PUBLIC)
Douglaston,NY
Course

GOLF COURSE 718 428-1617
TEE TIMES 718 224-6566

HOLES	YARDS blue\white\red	PAR	RATING blue\white\red	SLOPE blue\white\red
18	5585\5140\4602	67	65.4\63.7\62.1	103\101\101

HOLES	1	2	3	4	5	6	7	8	9	TOTAL
PAR	4	3	4	4	3	4	5	4	3	34
YARDS	341	143	332	416	125	367	470	376	170	2740
(Blue)	381	163	365	431	140	417	505	385	200	2987

HOLES	10	11	12	13	14	15	16	17	18	TOTAL
PAR	4	4	3	4	4	3	3	3	5	33
YARDS	304	275	146	370	377	166	154	113	495	2400
(Blue)	324	295	166	390	387	178	175	133	550	2598

GREEN FEES:$18 on weekdays,$20 weekends.**First Tee Off:**Dawn.**Tee Times:**Call 10
(Resident)   days prior for weekend,7 days prior for weeday.There is a $2 reservation
fee per golfer.
GREEN FEES:$24 on weekdays,$26 on weekends.
(Non-resident)

ARCHITECT:N\A
YEAR BUILT:N\A
PRO: Helen Finn,PGA
SEASON: All year

DISCOUNTS: Seniors and Twilight
CART FEES:$25,Pull carts $3
SPIKE POLICY: Spikes or soft spikes
AVAILABLE FOR TOURNAMENTS:yes
CONTACT: Bob or Scott **DAYS:**Mon-Sun
min 20-max none.

COURSE DESCRIPTION: This is a short tree-lined,hilly course with 7 par 3's.

FEATURES\FACILITIES:
DRIVING RANGE-no
RESTAURANT-yes
LOUNGE-no
LESSONS-yes
PRO SHOP-yes

BANQUET-no
WOMEN'S LOCKERS-no
MEN'S LOCKERS-yes
MEETING ROOM-no
NEARBY LODGING-yes

PRACTICE AREA-yes
BAR-no
RENTAL CLUBS-yes
CREDIT CARDS-yes
SNACK BAR-yes

DIRECTIONS:495 LIE to exit 31.Make a right onto Marathon Parkway and follow signs
to course.

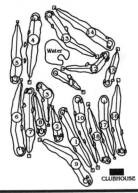

DYKER BEACH GC (PUBLIC)
Brooklyn,NY
Course

GOLF COURSE 718 836-9722
TEE TIMES 718 225-4653

HOLES	YARDS blue\white\red	PAR	RATING blue\white\red	SLOPE blue\white\red
18	6548\6260\5696	71	70.5\69.2\00.0	116\114\000

HOLES	1	2	3	4	5	6	7	8	9	TOTAL
PAR	4	3	4	4	4	5	4	3	4	35
YARDS	376	150	346	438	418	450	365	195	379	3117
(Blue)	393	163	369	447	427	461	379	211	401	3251

HOLES	10	11	12	13	14	15	16	17	18	TOTAL
PAR	4	3	4	5	4	3	5	4	4	36
YARDS	417	187	338	428	412	170	488	363	340	3143
(Blue)	423	201	358	493	423	183	494	374	348	3297

GREEN FEES:$18 on weekdays,$20 weekends.**First Tee Off:**Dawn.**Tee Times:**Call 10
(Resident) days prior.There is a $2 reservation fee per golfer.

GREEN FEES:$25 on weekdays,$26 on weekends.
(Non-resident)

ARCHITECT: John Van Kleek
YEAR BUILT:1935
PRO: Jeff Contraty
SEASON: All year

DISCOUNTS: Twilight
CART FEES:$24\$25
SPIKE POLICY: Spikes or soft spikes
AVAILABLE FOR TOURNAMENTS:yes
CONTACT: Jeff Contraty **DAYS:**Mon-Sun,64 golfers.
Weekends after 11am.

COURSE DESCRIPTION: Wide open course,not very long.Excellent greens.

FEATURES\FACILITIES:
DRIVING RANGE-no
RESTAURANT-no
LOUNGE-no
LESSONS-yes
PRO SHOP-yes

BANQUET-no
WOMEN'S LOCKERS-yes
MEN'S LOCKERS-yes
MEETING ROOM-no
NEARBY LODGING-no

PRACTICE AREA-yes
BAR-no
RENTAL CLUBS-yes
CREDIT CARDS-yes
SNACK BAR-yes

DIRECTIONS: Belt Parkway Westbound to exit 4 (14th Ave/Bay 8th St).At first traffic
light make a left.Proceed to next traffic light and make a left,bear right around course to
86th Street and Course entrance.

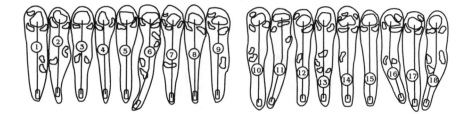

EISENHOWER PARK   (PUBLIC)

East Meadow,NY

Blue Course

GOLF COURSE 516 572-0327

TEE TIMES 516 542-4653

HOLES	YARDS blue\white\red	PAR	RATING blue\white\red	SLOPE blue\white\red
18	0000\6026\0000	72	00.0\68.0\00.0	000\112\000

HOLES	1	2	3	4	5	6	7	8	9	TOTAL
PAR	5	4	4	3	4	5	4	3	4	36
YARDS	458	354	405	172	372	445	342	114	357	3019
(Blue)	000	000	000	000	000	000	000	000	000	0000

HOLES	10	11	12	13	14	15	16	17	18	TOTAL
PAR	4	5	4	4	4	3	4	3	5	36
YARDS	382	460	342	309	370	172	387	129	456	3007
(Blue)	000	000	000	000	000	000	000	000	000	0000

GREEN FEES:$14 on weekdays,$16 weekends.**First Tee Off:**Dawn.**Tee Times:**Leisure
(Resident) pass holders can call 7 days in advance.There is a $4 reservation fee per golfer.Reservations start at 10am.

GREEN FEES:$28 on weekdays,$32 on weekends.Must be accompanied by resident.
(Non-resident)

ARCHITECT:N\A
YEAR BUILT:1920's
PRO: Sal Silverstone,PGA
SEASON: All year

DISCOUNTS: Seniors,Twilight,Vol.Firefighters
CART FEES:$32
SPIKE POLICY: Soft spikes required
AVAILABLE FOR TOURNAMENTS:no

COURSE DESCRIPTION: Fairly flat course with elevated greens.Well bunkered.

FEATURES\FACILITIES:

DRIVING RANGE-yes
RESTAURANT-yes
LOUNGE-yes
LESSONS-yes
PRO SHOP-yes

BANQUET-yes
WOMEN'S LOCKERS-yes
MEN'S LOCKERS-yes
MEETING ROOM-yes
NEARBY LODGING-yes

PRACTICE AREA-yes
BAR-yes
RENTAL CLUBS-yes
CREDIT CARDS-no
SNACK BAR-yes

DIRECTIONS:495 LIE to exit 38 (Northern State Parkway).Proceed to the Meadowbrook Parkway.Exit at Stewart Ave.Take to Park entrance and Course.

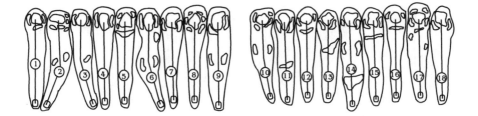

EISENHOWER PARK   (PUBLIC)

East Meadow,NY

Red Course

GOLF COURSE 516 572-0327

TEE TIMES 516 542-4653

HOLES	YARDS blue\white\red	PAR	RATING blue\white\red	SLOPE blue\white\red
18	6794\6357\5504	72	71.5\69.7\70.7	121\117\111

HOLES	1	2	3	4	5	6	7	8	9	TOTAL
PAR	5	4	4	4	3	4	4	4	4	36
YARDS	462	266	420	418	130	385	405	336	334	3156
(Blue)	488	277	451	444	143	430	424	374	338	3369

HOLES	10	11	12	13	14	15	16	17	18	TOTAL
PAR	4	4	5	3	4	4	3	5	4	36
YARDS	405	292	461	193	365	402	150	514	419	3201
(Blue)	421	312	493	211	369	450	166	556	447	3425

GREEN FEES:$14 on weekdays,$16 weekends.**First Tee Off:**Dawn.**Tee Times:**Leisure
(Resident)   pass holders can call 7 days in advance.There is a $4 reservation fee per
golfer.Reservations start at 10am.

GREEN FEES:$28 on weekdays,$32 on weekends.Must be accompanied by resident.
(Non-resident)

ARCHITECT:N\A
YEAR BUILT:1920's
PRO: Sal Silverstone,PGA
SEASON: All year

DISCOUNTS: Seniors,Twilight,Vol.Firefighters
CART FEES:$32
SPIKE POLICY: Soft spikes required
AVAILABLE FOR TOURNAMENTS:no

COURSE DESCRIPTION: Fairly flat course with elevated greens.Well bunkered.

FEATURES\FACILITIES:
DRIVING RANGE-yes
RESTAURANT-yes
LOUNGE-yes
LESSONS-yes
PRO SHOP-yes

BANQUET-yes
WOMEN'S LOCKERS-yes
MEN'S LOCKERS-yes
MEETING ROOM-yes
NEARBY LODGING-yes

PRACTICE AREA-yes
BAR-yes
RENTAL CLUBS-yes
CREDIT CARDS-no
SNACK BAR-yes

DIRECTIONS:495 LIE to exit 38 (Northern State Parkway).Proceed to the Meadowbrook
Parkway.Exit at Stewart Ave.Take to Park entrance and Course.

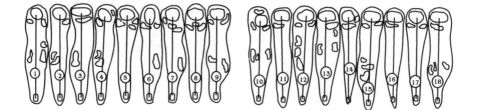

EISENHOWER PARK (PUBLIC)
East Meadow,NY
White Course

GOLF COURSE 516 572-0327
TEE TIMES 516 542-4653

HOLES	YARDS blue\white\red	PAR	RATING blue\white\red	SLOPE blue\white\red
18	0000\6269\0000	72	00.0\69.2\71.6	000\117\116

HOLES	1	2	3	4	5	6	7	8	9	TOTAL
PAR	4	4	5	4	3	4	5	3	4	36
YARDS	366	360	510	386	179	360	468	148	388	3165
(Blue)	000	000	000	000	000	000	000	000	000	0000

HOLES	10	11	12	13	14	15	16	17	18	TOTAL
PAR	4	4	5	4	3	4	4	3	5	36
YARDS	396	323	475	347	141	399	380	183	460	3104
(Blue)	000	000	000	000	000	000	000	000	000	0000

GREEN FEES:$14 on weekdays,$16 weekends.**First Tee Off:**Dawn.**Tee Times:**Leisure
(Resident) pass holders can call 7 days in advance.There is a $4 reservation fee per golfer.Reservations start at 10am.

GREEN FEES:$28 on weekdays,$32 on weekends.Must be accompanied by resident.
(Non-resident)

ARCHITECT:N\A
YEAR BUILT:1920's
PRO: Sal Silverstone,PGA
SEASON: All year

DISCOUNTS: Seniors,Twilight,Vol.Firefighters
CART FEES:$32
SPIKE POLICY: Soft spikes required
AVAILABLE FOR TOURNAMENTS:no

COURSE DESCRIPTION: Fairly flat and straight.Good course for beginners.

FEATURES\FACILITIES:
DRIVING RANGE-yes
RESTAURANT-yes
LOUNGE-yes
LESSONS-yes
PRO SHOP-yes

BANQUET-yes
WOMEN'S LOCKERS-yes
MEN'S LOCKERS-yes
MEETING ROOM-yes
NEARBY LODGING-yes

PRACTICE AREA-yes
BAR-yes
RENTAL CLUBS-yes
CREDIT CARDS-no
SNACK BAR-yes

DIRECTIONS: 495 LIE to exit 38 (Northern State Parkway).Proceed to the Meadowbrook
Parkway.Exit at Stewart Ave.Take to Park entrance and Course.

NO LAYOUT AVAILABLE

FLUSHING MEADOW GC

GOLF COURSE 718 271-8182

Corona,NY   (PUBLIC)
Pitch and Putt

HOLES	YARDS blue\white\red	PAR	RATING blue\white\red	SLOPE blue\white\red
18	0000\0990\0000	54	00.0\00.0\00.0	000\000\000

HOLES	1	2	3	4	5	6	7	8	9	TOTAL
PAR	3	3	3	3	3	3	3	3	3	27
YARDS	80	40	50	65	45	65	55	50	80	530
(Blue)	000	000	000	000	000	000	000	000	000	0000

HOLES	10	11	12	13	14	15	16	17	18	TOTAL
PAR	3	3	3	3	3	3	3	3	3	27
YARDS	40	50	45	50	50	60	60	55	50	460
(Blue)	000	000	000	000	000	000	000	000	000	0000

GREEN FEES:$7.25 on weekdays,$8.25 weekends.**First Tee Off:**8am.**Tee Times:**First come,first serve.

ARCHITECT: New York City
YEAR BUILT:1966
PRO: Owen Bailey,PGA
SEASON: All year

DISCOUNTS: Seniors and Juniors ($6 weekdays)
CART FEES: No carts
SPIKE POLICY: Spikes or soft spikes
AVAILABLE FOR TOURNAMENTS:yes
CONTACT: Jerry **DAYS:**Mon-Sun
min 20-max 72.

COURSE DESCRIPTION: This is a pitch and putt course.Great for beginners and to practice your short game.

FEATURES\FACILITIES:

DRIVING RANGE-no
RESTAURANT-no
LOUNGE-no
LESSONS-yes
PRO SHOP-no

BANQUET-no
WOMEN'S LOCKERS-no
MEN'S LOCKERS-no
MEETING ROOM-no
NEARBY LODGING-yes

PRACTICE AREA-yes
BAR-no
RENTAL CLUBS-yes
CREDIT CARDS-no
SNACK BAR-yes

DIRECTIONS: Golf course is located inside Flushing Meadow Park.

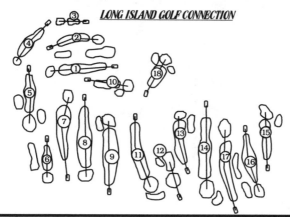

FOREST PARK GC (PUBLIC)

Woodhaven,NY

Course

GOLF COURSE 718 296-0999

TEE TIMES 718 296-0999

HOLES	YARDS blue\white\red	PAR	RATING blue\white\red	SLOPE blue\white\red
18	5820\5431\0000	67	67.5\65.5\69.5	111\108\116

HOLES	1	2	3	4	5	6	7	8	9	TOTAL
PAR	4	4	3	4	4	3	4	4	4	34
YARDS	423	381	112	247	362	162	365	415	396	2863
(Blue)	443	400	123	323	375	171	390	433	414	3072

HOLES	10	11	12	13	14	15	16	17	18	TOTAL
PAR	3	4	3	4	4	4	4	4	3	33
YARDS	190	362	137	294	435	293	331	365	161	2568
(Blue)	196	390	143	319	461	308	349	410	172	2748

GREEN FEES:$17 on weekdays,$19 weekends.**First Tee Off:**Dawn.**Tee Times:**Call 7
(Resident)   days prior.There is a $2 reservation fee per golfer.

GREEN FEES:$23 on weekdays,$25 on weekends.
(Non-resident)

ARCHITECT: Art Bartelow
YEAR BUILT:1901
PRO: Paul Giordano,PGA
SEASON: All year

DISCOUNTS: Seniors and Twilight
CART FEES:$24.50\$25.50
SPIKE POLICY: Spikes or soft spikes
AVAILABLE FOR TOURNAMENTS:yes
CONTACT: Paul Giordano **DAYS:**Weekdays
no min-max 120.Weekends start after 10am,max
60 golfers.

COURSE DESCRIPTION: Tree-lined,challenging,shotmakers course.New Clubhouse
added this year.

FEATURES\FACILITIES:

DRIVING RANGE-no	BANQUET-yes	PRACTICE AREA-yes
RESTAURANT-yes	WOMEN'S LOCKERS-no	BAR-yes
LOUNGE-yes	MEN'S LOCKERS-no	RENTAL CLUBS-yes
LESSONS-yes	MEETING ROOM-yes	CREDIT CARDS-yes
PRO SHOP-yes	NEARBY LODGING-yes	SNACK BAR-yes

DIRECTIONS: Interborough Parkway to the Forest Park exit.Course is on the left after
exit.Course has supervised parking.

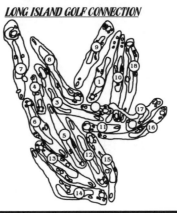

FOX HILL GC   (PUBLIC)   GOLF COURSE 516 369-0160
Baiting Hallow,NY
   Course

HOLES	YARDS blue\white\red	PAR	RATING blue\white\red	SLOPE blue\white\red
18	6838\6365\5522	72	73.8\71.8\73.0	130\124\126

HOLES	1	2	3	4	5	6	7	8	9	TOTAL
PAR	4	3	4	3	4	4	5	4	4	35
YARDS	388	149	444	202	329	363	500	385	364	3124
(Blue)	430	178	450	230	375	390	525	401	384	3363

HOLES	10	11	12	13	14	15	16	17	18	TOTAL
PAR	5	3	4	4	5	4	4	3	5	37
YARDS	453	152	380	338	477	391	406	166	478	3241
(Blue)	493	172	402	363	493	408	462	187	495	3475

GREEN FEES:$50 on weekdays,$80 weekends.**First Tee Off:**Dawn.**Tee Times:**Call 2
(Members)   weeks prior with Fox Hill card.

GREEN FEES:$70 on weekdays,$110 weekends.**First Tee Off:**Dawn.**Tee Times:**Call 7
(Non-members) days prior.

ARCHITECT: Robert Trent Jones   **DISCOUNTS:**Call for details
YEAR BUILT:1963   **CART FEES:**Included
PRO: John Hines,PGA   **SPIKE POLICY:**Soft spikes required
SEASON: April-Nov.   **AVAILABLE FOR TOURNAMENTS:**yes
                                    CONTACT: John Hines **DAYS:**Mon-Thurs,no min,
                                    no max (call for details).

COURSE DESCRIPTION:1998 season host for the NYS Open.Exceptionally challenging,
qualifier for the US Open.Over 6800 yards from the back tees.Water comes into play on
4 holes.

FEATURES\FACILITIES:
DRIVING RANGE-yes   BANQUET-yes   PRACTICE AREA-yes
RESTAURANT-yes   WOMEN'S LOCKERS-yes   BAR-yes
LOUNGE-yes   MEN'S LOCKERS-yes   RENTAL CLUBS-yes
LESSONS-yes   MEETING ROOM-yes   CREDIT CARDS-yes
PRO SHOP-yes   NEARBY LODGING-yes   SNACK BAR-yes

DIRECTIONS:495 LIE to exit 71.Make a left on Edwards Ave.Proceed to Sound Ave and
make a right.Proceed to Oakleigh Ave and make a left.Course entrance is ½ mile on the
right.

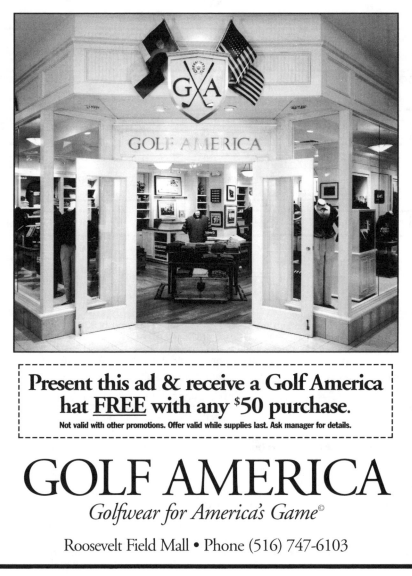

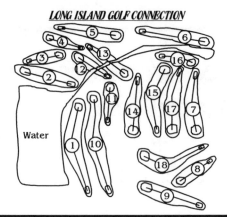

GLEN COVE GC   (PUBLIC)

Glen Cove,NY

Course

GOLF COURSE 516 671-0033
TEE TIMES 516 676-0550

HOLES	YARDS blue\white\red	PAR	RATING blue\white\red	SLOPE blue\white\red
18	0000\4815\4148	66	00.0\63.2\63.2	000\108\106

HOLES	1	2	3	4	5	6	7	8	9	TOTAL
PAR	5	4	3	3	4	4	4	3	3	33
YARDS	478	376	157	173	307	357	374	115	187	2524
(Blue)	000	000	000	000	000	000	000	000	000	0000

HOLES	10	11	12	13	14	15	16	17	18	TOTAL
PAR	4	3	3	4	4	4	3	4	4	33
YARDS	447	157	212	254	242	326	163	263	227	2291
(Blue)	000	000	000	000	000	000	000	000	000	0000

GREEN FEES: $12 on weekdays,$14 weekends.**First Tee Off:**Dawn.**Tee Times:**Call 7 days
(Resident)   in advance.You must have course permit.Permit is $30 for season.Course
does sell season passes for unlimited play.Call for details.

GREEN FEES: $14 on weekdays,$16 on weekends.Membership is not restricted to Town
(Non-resident)   residents,but permit fees are required for all.Call for details.

ARCHITECT: Bill Mitchell
YEAR BUILT:1970
PRO: Howard Robertson,PGA
SEASON: March-December

DISCOUNTS: Resident Seniors,Juniors
CART FEES:$22
SPIKE POLICY: Soft spikes required
AVAILABLE FOR TOURNAMENTS:yes
CONTACT: John Simon **DAYS:**Mondays only,
min 72-max 200.

COURSE DESCRIPTION: Short but very challenging course.Fast greens with a few water holes.

FEATURES\FACILITIES:

DRIVING RANGE-yes
RESTAURANT-yes
LOUNGE-yes
LESSONS-yes
PRO SHOP-yes

BANQUET-no
WOMEN'S LOCKERS-yes
MEN'S LOCKERS-yes
MEETING ROOM-no
NEARBY LODGING-no

PRACTICE AREA-yes
BAR-yes
RENTAL CLUBS-yes
CREDIT CARDS-yes
SNACK BAR-yes

DIRECTIONS:495 LIE to exit 39 North.(Glen Cove Rd).Proceed to fork and bear left onto
Route 107.At the firehouse make a right onto Brewster St.Proceed ½ mile to Dosoris Ln
and make a left.Proceed on Dosoris Ln for 1 ½ miles to Lattingtown Rd and make a right.
Course is on the left.

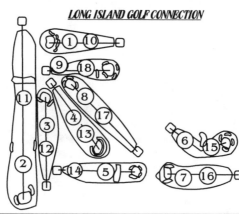

GULL HAVEN GC (PUBLIC)

GOLF COURSE 516 436-6059

Central Islip,NY

9 Hole Course (play twice for 18)

HOLES	YARDS blue\white\red	PAR	RATING blue\white\red	SLOPE blue\white\red
18	0000\5568\5260	70	00.0\66.5\69.8	000\105\107

HOLES	1	2	3	4	5	6	7	8	9	TOTAL
PAR	4	4	4	3	3	4	4	4	4	34
YARDS	290	465	330	140	155	350	355	340	280	2705
(Blue)	000	000	000	000	000	000	000	000	000	0000

HOLES	10	11	12	13	14	15	16	17	18	TOTAL
PAR	4	5	4	3	4	4	4	4	4	36
YARDS	000	000	000	000	000	000	000	000	000	0000
(Blue)	290	510	330	148	260	350	355	340	280	2863

GREEN FEES:$12 on weekdays,$14 weekends.**First Tee Off:**6:30am.**Tee Times:**First
(Resident)   come,first serve.18 hole fee on 9 hole course.

GREEN FEES:$15 on weekdays,$18 on weekends.**First Tee Off:**6:30am.**Tee Times:**First
(Non-resident)   come,first serve.

ARCHITECT:N\A
YEAR BUILT:1930's
PRO: Doug Jansen,PGA
SEASON: All year

DISCOUNTS: Resident seniors,Twilight
CART FEES:$16,Pull carts $3
SPIKE POLICY: Soft spikes required
AVAILABLE FOR TOURNAMENTS:yes
Contact: Doug Jansen **Days:**Mon-Thurs
Call for details.

COURSE DESCRIPTION:9 hole course.Play it twice for 18.Front 9 from white tees,back
9 from blue tees.Fairly straight course with opened fairways and well bunkered.

FEATURES\FACILITIES:
DRIVING RANGE-no
RESTAURANT-no
LOUNGE-no
LESSONS-yes
PRO SHOP-yes

BANQUET-no
WOMEN'S LOCKERS-no
MEN'S LOCKERS-no
MEETING ROOM-no
NEARBY LODGING-no

PRACTICE AREA-YES
BAR-no
RENTAL CLUBS-no
CREDIT CARDS-no
SNACK BAR-yes

DIRECTIONS:495 LIE to exit 56.South on Route 111.At fork stay left onto Wheeler Ave.
Wheeler turns into Carlton Ave.Proceed to Gull Haven Dr and make a left to course.

WE'LL GIVE YOU 18 GOOD REASONS TO PLAY HERE.

ANNUAL MEMBERSHIPS AVAILABLE AT THE HAMLET WIND WATCH GOLF CLUB

Boasting beautiful fairways, obsessively manicured greens, more than 70 bunkers filled with imported white sand and a slope rating of 128, the newly renovated par 71 Hamlet Wind Watch Golf Club offers you premium accessibility to tee times, club amenities, tournaments or just a great opportunity to enjoy a day in the sun.

In addition, Annual Membership includes green fees, access to a USGA Handicap, discounts to all merchandise at the new Pro Shop and pool and tennis privileges.

For more information about the many benefits of an Annual Membership, please call Pat Dill, Director of Golf, at 516-232-9850.

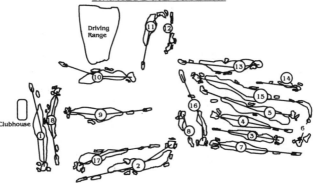

LONG ISLAND GOLF CONNECTION

HAMLET WINDWATCH GC

Hauppauge, NY   (PUBLIC)

Course

GOLF COURSE 516 232-9850
TEE TIMES 516 232-9850

HOLES	YARDS blue\white\red	PAR	RATING blue\white\red	SLOPE blue\white\red
18	6425\6138\5135	71	71.0\69.7\68.6	128\125\118

HOLES	1	2	3	4	5	6	7	8	9	TOTAL
PAR	4	5	4	4	5	3	4	3	4	36
YARDS	348	512	337	380	478	179	424	169	391	3218
(Blue)	353	550	349	396	495	186	435	190	406	3360

HOLES	10	11	12	13	14	15	16	17	18	TOTAL
PAR	4	4	3	4	3	5	4	4	4	35
YARDS	324	306	150	387	222	545	329	379	362	3024
(Blue)	340	341	155	399	245	556	338	395	382	3149

GREEN FEES:$62 on weekdays,$72 weekends.**First Tee Off:**7am\6am.**Tee Times:**Call 3 days prior.Cart fees are included and mandatory.

ARCHITECT: Joe Lee
YEAR BUILT:1989
PRO: Sean Mulligan,PGA
SEASON: All year

DISCOUNTS: Twilight
CART FEES: Included
SPIKE POLICY: Soft spikes required
AVAILABLE FOR TOURNAMENTS:yes
CONTACT: Scott Cronin **DAYS:**Mon or Tues,72 players,Wed or Thurs,12-60 players.Shotgun starts are available.Call for details.

COURSE DESCRIPTION: Florida style course.Tight and well bunkered with a lot of water holes.

FEATURES\FACILITIES:
DRIVING RANGE-yes
RESTAURANT-yes
LOUNGE-yes
LESSONS-yes
PRO SHOP-yes

BANQUET-yes
WOMEN'S LOCKERS-yes
MEN'S LOCKERS-yes
MEETING ROOM-yes
NEARBY LODGING-yes

PRACTICE AREA-yes
BAR-yes
RENTAL CLUBS-yes
CREDIT CARDS-yes
SNACK BAR-yes

DIRECTIONS:495 LIE to exit 57.Proceed approx. 1 mile to Veterans Memorial Highway and make a left.Proceed ¼ mile to Motor Parkway and make a right.Proceed to Wyndam Hotel and course on the left.

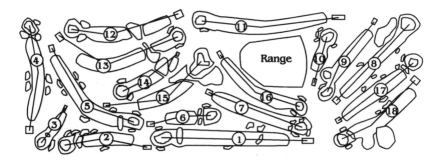

HAUPPAUGE CC (SEMI-PRIVATE)

GOLF COURSE 516 724-7500

Hauppauge,NY

Course

HOLES	YARDS blue\white\red	PAR	RATING blue\white\red	SLOPE blue\white\red
18	6525\6280\5925	72	71.0\69.9\75.5	122\120\131

HOLES	1	2	3	4	5	6	7	8	9	TOTAL
PAR	5	4	3	4	5	3	4	4	4	36
YARDS	493	300	124	351	474	179	350	400	355	3026
(Blue)	507	310	134	364	487	192	372	412	366	3144

HOLES	10	11	12	13	14	15	16	17	18	TOTAL
PAR	3	5	4	5	3	4	4	4	4	36
YARDS	173	539	407	473	184	360	370	375	373	3254
(Blue)	184	551	417	495	195	370	394	388	387	3381

GREEN FEES:$55 on weekdays,$70 on weekends.Cart fees are included and mandatory. **First Tee Off:**6am on weekdays,3pm on weekends.Course is closed to non-members on weekends until 3pm.

ARCHITECT:N\A
YEAR BUILT:1960
PRO: Kevin Beatty,PGA
SEASON: All year

DISCOUNTS: Seniors and Twilight
CART FEES: Included
SPIKE POLICY: Soft spikes preferred
AVAILABLE FOR TOURNAMENTS:yes
CONTACT: Kevin Beatty **DAYS:**Mon-Fri min 30-max 144.

COURSE DESCRIPTION: Flat but challenging course with water on most of the back 9.

FEATURES\FACILITIES:
DRIVING RANGE-yes
RESTAURANT-yes
LOUNGE-no
LESSONS-yes
PRO SHOP-yes

BANQUET-yes
WOMEN'S LOCKERS-yes
MEN'S LOCKERS-yes
MEETING ROOM-yes
NEARBY LODGING-yes

PRACTICE AREA-yes
BAR-yes
RENTAL CLUBS-yes
CREDIT CARDS-yes
SNACK BAR-yes

DIRECTIONS:495 LIE to exit 56.Proceed North on Route 111 to Veterans Highway and make a left.Course is ¼ mile on the right.

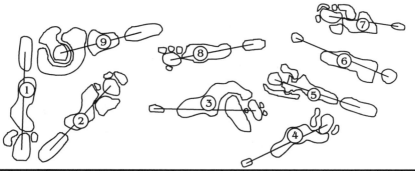

HEARTLAND GOLF PARK

Edgewood,NY   (PUBLIC)

GOLF COURSE 516 667-7400

Course

HOLES	YARDS blue\white\red	PAR	RATING blue\white\red	SLOPE blue\white\red
9	1220\1079\930	27	00.0\00.0\00.0	000\000\000

HOLES	1	2	3	4	5	6	7	8	9	TOTAL
PAR	3	3	3	3	3	3	3	3	3	27
YARDS	121	119	139	118	123	140	95	109	115	1079
(Blue)	138	136	155	128	140	158	107	126	132	1220

HOLES	10	11	12	13	14	15	16	17	18	TOTAL
PAR	0	0	0	0	0	0	0	0	0	00
YARDS	000	000	000	000	000	000	000	000	000	0000
(Blue)	000	000	000	000	000	000	000	000	000	0000

GREEN FEES:$10 on weekdays,$12 on weekends.**Tee Times:**First come,first serve. (7am-7pm)

GREEN FEES:$20 on weekdays,$20 on weekends.**Tee Times:**First come,first serve. (7pm-7am)

ARCHITECT: Multiple
YEAR BUILT:1995
PRO: Pat Diesu,PGA
SEASON: All year

DISCOUNTS: Seniors
CART FEES: Pull carts $2
SPIKE POLICY: Soft spikes required
AVAILABLE FOR TOURNAMENTS:yes
CONTACT: David Wolkoff 516 242-6300
DAYS: Mondays peferred,max 36 players. Shotgun starts available.

COURSE DESCRIPTION: This course is opened 24 hours.Each hole is designed after famous par 3's.

FEATURES\FACILITIES:

DRIVING RANGE-yes	BANQUET-yes	PRACTICE AREA-yes
RESTAURANT-yes	WOMEN'S LOCKERS-no	BAR-yes
LOUNGE-no	MEN'S LOCKERS-no	RENTAL CLUBS-yes
LESSONS-yes	MEETING ROOM-no	CREDIT CARDS-yes
PRO SHOP-yes	NEARBY LODGING-yes	SNACK BAR-yes

DIRECTIONS:495 LIE to Exit 52 South (Commack Rd).Proceed to Long Island Ave and make a left.Proceed to course.

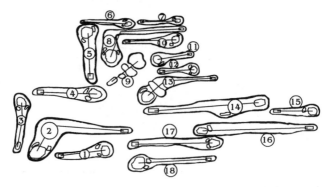

HEATHERWOOD GC
Centereach,NY (PUBLIC)
Course

GOLF COURSE 516 473-9000
TEE TIMES 516 473-9000

HOLES	YARDS blue\white\red	PAR	RATING blue\white\red	SLOPE blue\white\red
18	0000\4089\3395	60	00.0\58.6\58.5	000\095\091

HOLES	1	2	3	4	5	6	7	8	9	TOTAL
PAR	3	4	3	3	4	3	3	4	3	30
YARDS	158	351	200	194	336	161	151	379	148	2078
(Blue)	000	000	000	000	000	000	000	000	000	0000

HOLES	10	11	12	13	14	15	16	17	18	TOTAL
PAR	3	3	3	4	4	3	4	3	3	30
YARDS	190	171	119	278	388	135	370	193	167	2011
(Blue)	000	000	000	000	000	000	000	000	000	0000

GREEN FEES:$20 on weekdays,$22 weekends.**First Tee Off:**6am\5:30am.**Tee Times:**You must be on reservation list;fee is $16 for season.Call 3 days in advance for a $4 charge.Guaranteed starting times for weekends are available.

ARCHITECT:N\A
YEAR BUILT:1960's
PRO: Bob Freund
SEASON: All year

DISCOUNTS: Seniors and Twilight
CART FEES:$22
SPIKE POLICY: Spikes or soft spikes
AVAILABLE FOR TOURNAMENTS:yes
CONTACT: Bob or John **DAYS:**Mon-Sun,no outings on weekends after Memorial day.Min 20-max 75.

COURSE DESCRIPTION: Intermediate course,one or two water holes,well bunkered,6 holes over 200 yards.

FEATURES\FACILITIES:

DRIVING RANGE-no
RESTAURANT-yes
LOUNGE-no
LESSONS-yes
PRO SHOP-yes

BANQUET-no
WOMEN'S LOCKERS-no
MEN'S LOCKERS-yes
MEETING ROOM-no
NEARBY LODGING-no

PRACTICE AREA-yes
BAR-yes
RENTAL CLUBS-yes
CREDIT CARDS-yes
SNACK BAR-yes

DIRECTIONS:495 LIE to exit 62 North.(Nicholls Rd).Proceed to Route 347 and make a right.Proceed 1 ½ miles to course on the right.

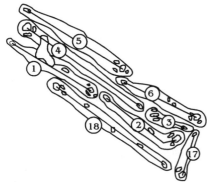 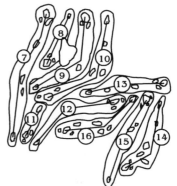

HOLBROOK CC   (PUBLIC)

Holbrook,NY

GOLF COURSE 516 467-3417

TEE TIMES 516 224-5648

Course

HOLES	YARDS blue\white\red	PAR	RATING blue\white\red	SLOPE blue\white\red
18	6252\5978\4736	71	69.8\68.5\66.9	128\126\119

HOLES	1	2	3	4	5	6	7	8	9	TOTAL
PAR	4	4	3	5	4	4	5	3	4	36
YARDS	350	321	133	516	420	309	490	192	370	3101
(Blue)	365	337	143	531	436	322	536	207	380	3257

HOLES	10	11	12	13	14	15	16	17	18	TOTAL
PAR	4	3	4	4	4	4	4	3	5	35
YARDS	423	127	383	311	311	368	300	166	488	2877
(Blue)	428	138	393	326	325	397	309	179	500	2995

GREEN FEES:$18 on weekdays,$20 weekends.**First Tee Off:**7am.**Tee Times:**Call 7
(Residents)   days prior for Saturday and Sunday.Weekday call same day.

GREEN FEES:$23 on weekdays,$28 on weekends.
(Non-resident)

ARCHITECT: Ward Associates
YEAR BUILT:1992
PRO: Bill LePosa,PGA
SEASON: March-December

DISCOUNTS: Resident Seniors,Twilight for all.
CART FEES:$26,Pull $3.50
SPIKE POLICY: Soft spikes required
AVAILABLE FOR TOURNAMENTS:yes
CONTACT: Brenda 516 224-5419 **DAYS:**Tues.
Only,shotgun starts min 100-max 144.

COURSE DESCRIPTION: Short,tight,challenging course with elevated greens and 4
water holes.

FEATURES\FACILITIES:

DRIVING RANGE-yes
RESTAURANT-yes
LOUNGE-yes
LESSONS-yes
PRO SHOP-yes

BANQUET-yes
WOMEN'S LOCKERS-yes
MEN'S LOCKERS-yes
MEETING ROOM-yes
NEARBY LODGING-yes

PRACTICE AREA-yes
BAR-yes
RENTAL CLUBS-no
CREDIT CARDS-yes
SNACK BAR-yes

DIRECTIONS:495 LIE to exit 61 South.Procced 1.9 miles to course on the right.

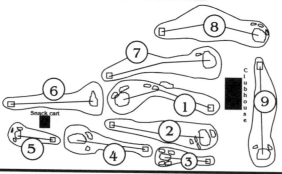

HOLLOW HILLS CC
Dix Hills,NY   (SEMI-PRIVATE)

GOLF COURSE 516 242-0010
TEE TIMES 516 242-0010

Course

HOLES	YARDS blue\white\red	PAR	RATING blue\white\red	SLOPE blue\white\red
9	2482\2341\2180	35	00.0\00.0\00.0	000\000\000

HOLES	1	2	3	4	5	6	7	8	9	TOTAL
PAR	4	5	3	4	3	4	4	4	4	35
YARDS	350	420	115	305	96	225	265	305	240	2341
(Blue)	365	440	135	315	102	265	295	315	260	2482

HOLES	10	11	12	13	14	15	16	17	18	TOTAL
PAR	0	0	0	0	0	0	0	0	0	00
YARDS	000	000	000	000	000	000	000	000	000	0000
(Blue)	000	000	000	000	000	000	000	000	000	0000

GREEN FEES: Included in membership.Call for details.
(Members)

GREEN FEES:$12 on weekdays,$15 on weekends.**First Tee Off:**6am.**Tee Times:**Call
(Non-members) 7 days in advance.There is a $3 reservation fee per golfer.

ARCHITECT:N\A
YEAR BUILT:1973
PRO: Ron Bifulco
SEASON: All year

DISCOUNTS: Seniors
CART FEES:$18
SPIKE POLICY: Soft spikes required
AVAILABLE FOR TOURNAMENTS:yes
CONTACT: Alison Denlea **DAYS:**Call for details.

COURSE DESCRIPTION: This is a challenging,hilly and narrow course.

FEATURES\FACILITIES:
DRIVING RANGE-no
RESTAURANT-yes
LOUNGE-no
LESSONS-yes
PRO SHOP-yes

BANQUET-yes
WOMEN'S LOCKERS-no
MEN'S LOCKERS-no
MEETING ROOM-no
NEARBY LODGING-no

PRACTICE AREA-yes
BAR-yes
RENTAL CLUBS-yes
CREDIT CARDS-yes
SNACK BAR-yes

DIRECTIONS:495 LIE to exit 51.Proceed South approx. 1 mile to Ryder Ave and make a
right.Course is 1 mile on the left.

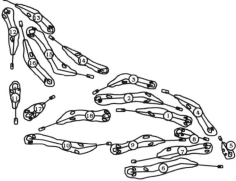

INDIAN ISLAND CC   (PUBLIC)

Riverhead,NY

Course

GOLF COURSE 516 727-7776

TEE TIMES 516 244-7275

HOLES	YARDS blue\white\red	PAR	RATING blue\white\red	SLOPE blue\white\red
18	6353\5976\5524	72	71.0\69.3\72.8	124\121\126

HOLES	1	2	3	4	5	6	7	8	9	TOTAL
PAR	4	5	4	4	3	5	4	3	4	36
YARDS	428	482	342	367	122	453	412	150	375	3131
(Blue)	437	499	362	384	167	496	429	168	393	3335

HOLES	10	11	12	13	14	15	16	17	18	TOTAL
PAR	5	3	4	4	4	5	4	3	4	36
YARDS	433	195	307	308	308	458	318	168	350	2845
(Blue)	454	212	328	329	322	485	336	185	367	3018

GREEN FEES:$22 on weekdays,$23 weekends.**First Tee Off:**6am.**Tee Times:**You must
(Resident)   be a Suffolk County resident with a Green Key Card.Card holders can call
7 days in advance or day before from a touch tone phone.There is a
$3 reservation fee per golfer.

GREEN FEES:$31 on weekdays,$35 on weekends.**Tee Times:**Non-residents can not call
(Non-resident)   for reservations.They must walk on.

ARCHITECT: Alfred Tull
YEAR BUILT:1972
PRO: Robert Fox,PGA
SEASON: March-January

DISCOUNTS: Seniors and Juniors
CART FEES:$27,Pull carts $3
SPIKE POLICY: Soft spikes required
AVAILABLE FOR TOURNAMENTS:yes
CONTACT: Robert Fox **DAYS:**Weds only,Shotgun
starts.Min 100,max 144.

COURSE DESCRIPTION: This is a flat course that borders the Peconic Bay.The front
is tight.Water comes into play on a few holes.

FEATURES\FACILITIES:
DRIVING RANGE-yes
RESTAURANT-yes
LOUNGE-yes
LESSONS-yes
PRO SHOP-yes

BANQUET-yes
WOMEN'S LOCKERS-yes
MEN'S LOCKERS-yes
MEETING ROOM-yes
NEARBY LODGING-yes

PRACTICE AREA-yes
BAR-yes
RENTAL CLUBS-yes
CREDIT CARDS-no
SNACK BAR-yes

DIRECTIONS:495 LIE to exit 71.Proceed South on Route 24 for approximately 7 miles to
Route 105 and make a left.Proceed over bridge to the course on the right.

NO LAYOUT AVAILABLE

ISLAND'S END GOLF+CC

Greenport,NY   (SEMI-PRIVATE)
Course

GOLF COURSE 516 477-0777
TEE TIMES 718 225-4653

HOLES	YARDS blue\white\red	PAR	RATING blue\white\red	SLOPE blue\white\red
18	6639\6274\5039	72	71.6\70.6\68.8	118\115\116

HOLES	1	2	3	4	5	6	7	8	9	TOTAL
PAR	4	4	3	5	3	4	3	5	4	35
YARDS	351	335	147	473	180	370	186	540	358	2940
(Blue)	369	360	163	484	200	407	212	555	375	3125

HOLES	10	11	12	13	14	15	16	17	18	TOTAL
PAR	4	3	5	4	5	4	3	5	4	37
YARDS	382	173	503	389	479	284	170	517	437	3334
(Blue)	391	197	515	409	497	304	210	526	465	3514

GREEN FEES:$29 on weekdays,$33 weekends.**First Tee Off:**6:30am.**Tee Times:**Non-members can call day before after 12pm.There is a $5 reservation fee per golfer.

ARCHITECT: George Heron
YEAR BUILT:1961
PRO: Chris Vedder,PGA
SEASON: All year

DISCOUNTS: None
CART FEES:$15 pp.
SPIKE POLICY: Soft spikes preferred
AVAILABLE FOR TOURNAMENTS:yes
CONTACT: Chris Vedder **DAYS:**Mon-Thurs,no tournaments on weekends.Min 20,max 110.

COURSE DESCRIPTION: This course is fairly open and flat.Wind generally comes into play.Beautiful views of the Long Island Sound.

FEATURES\FACILITIES:

DRIVING RANGE-yes	BANQUET-no	PRACTICE AREA-yes
RESTAURANT-yes	WOMEN'S LOCKERS-yes	BAR-yes
LOUNGE-yes	MEN'S LOCKERS-yes	RENTAL CLUBS-yes
LESSONS-yes	MEETING ROOM-yes	CREDIT CARDS-no
PRO SHOP-yes	NEARBY LODGING-yes	SNACK BAR-yes

DIRECTIONS:495 LIE to last exit.Proceed East on Route 58 until it joins Route 25. Proceed on Route 25 for 19 miles to course on the left.

NO LAYOUT AVAILABLE

JONES BEACH STATE PARK GC   GOLF COURSE 516 785-1600
Wantagh,NY   (PUBLIC)
Pitch and Putt

HOLES	YARDS blue\white\red	PAR	RATING blue\white\red	SLOPE blue\white\red
18	0000\1039\0000	54	00.0\00.0\00.0	000\000\000

HOLES	1	2	3	4	5	6	7	8	9	TOTAL
PAR	3	3	3	3	3	3	3	3	3	27
YARDS	35	39	53	55	41	52	57	70	77	479
(Blue)	000	000	000	000	000	000	000	000	000	0000

HOLES	10	11	12	13	14	15	16	17	18	TOTAL
PAR	3	3	3	3	3	3	3	3	3	27
YARDS	57	50	79	67	68	57	56	56	70	560
(Blue)	000	000	000	000	000	000	000	000	000	0000

GREEN FEES:$5 on weekdays and weekends.**First Tee Off:**9am.**Tee Times:**First come, first serve.

ARCHITECT:N\A
YEAR BUILT:1950's
PRO: None
SEASON: April-November

DISCOUNTS: Seniors
CART FEES:N\A
SPIKE POLICY: Spikes or soft spikes
AVAILABLE FOR TOURNAMENTS:no

COURSE DESCRIPTION:18 hole pitch and putt.

FEATURES\FACILITIES:
DRIVING RANGE-no
RESTAURANT-no
LOUNGE-no
LESSONS-no
PRO SHOP-no

BANQUET-no
WOMEN'S LOCKERS-no
MEN'S LOCKERS-no
MEETING ROOM-no
NEARBY LODGING-no

PRACTICE AREA-no
BAR-no
RENTAL CLUBS-yes
CREDIT CARDS-no
SNACK BAR-yes

DIRECTIONS:495 LIE to Wantagh Parkway South (Jones Beach).Follow signs to Jones Beach State Park (field 4 or 5 parking area).

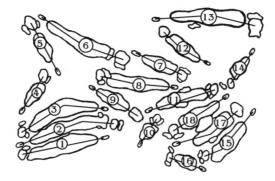

KISSENA PARK GC (PUBLIC)
Queens,NY
Course

GOLF COURSE 718 939-4594
TEE TIMES 718 939-4594

HOLES	YARDS blue\white\red	PAR	RATING blue\white\red	SLOPE blue\white\red
18	4665\4389\4087	64	61.7\60.9\63.9	94\ 93 \ 98

HOLES	1	2	3	4	5	6	7	8	9	TOTAL
PAR	4	4	4	3	3	4	3	4	3	32
YARDS	317	350	371	119	164	314	150	335	184	2304
(Blue)	330	370	416	122	169	322	162	346	198	2435

HOLES	10	11	12	13	14	15	16	17	18	TOTAL
PAR	3	4	3	4	3	4	3	4	4	32
YARDS	107	302	176	311	156	306	114	306	307	2085
(Blue)	117	317	199	331	166	329	124	329	318	2230

GREEN FEES:$17 on weekdays,$19 weekends.**First Tee Off:**Dawn.**Tee Times:**Call 10
(Residents)   days prior.There is a $2 reservation fee per golfer.

GREEN FEES:$23 on weekdays,$25 on weekends.
(Non-resident)

ARCHITECT:N\A
YEAR BUILT:1935
PRO: Paul Forest
SEASON: All year

DISCOUNTS: Seniors and Twilight
CART FEES:$24\$25
SPIKE POLICY: Spikes or soft spikes
AVAILABLE FOR TOURNAMENTS:yes
CONTACT: Paul Forest **DAYS:**Mon-Sun,no
min-max 170.

COURSE DESCRIPTION: Challenging executive course with great views of Manhattan
and Long Island.9th hole hardest par 3 in the City,200 yards uphill.

FEATURES\FACILITIES:
DRIVING RANGE-no   BANQUET-yes   PRACTICE AREA-yes
RESTAURANT-yes   WOMEN'S LOCKERS-no   BAR-yes
LOUNGE-yes   MEN'S LOCKERS-no   RENTAL CLUBS-yes
LESSONS-yes   MEETING ROOM-no   CREDIT CARDS-yes
PRO SHOP-yes   NEARBY LODGING-yes   SNACK BAR-yes

DIRECTIONS:495 LIE to exit 24 (Kissena Blvd).Make a right.Proceed 1 block to Booth
Memorial Ave and make a right.Course is on the left.

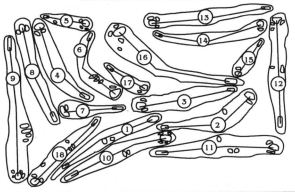

LIDO GC   (PUBLIC)
Lido Beach,NY

GOLF COURSE 516 889-8181
TEE TIMES 516 889-8181

Course

HOLES	YARDS blue\white\red	PAR	RATING blue\white\red	SLOPE blue\white\red
18	6868\6387\5603	71	00.0\71.1\71.4	000\128\114

HOLES	1	2	3	4	5	6	7	8	9	TOTAL
PAR	4	4	4	4	3	4	3	4	5	35
YARDS	439	347	315	356	157	346	193	387	552	3092
(Blue)	452	367	358	378	175	382	214	404	625	3355

HOLES	10	11	12	13	14	15	16	17	18	TOTAL
PAR	4	4	5	4	4	3	5	3	4	36
YARDS	396	385	502	413	376	166	460	189	408	3295
(Blue)	420	405	544	436	402	182	487	200	437	3513

GREEN FEES:$20 on weekdays,$25 on weekends.**First Tee Off:**Dawn.**Tee Times:**Call
(Residents)   one week in advance.There is a $5 reservation fee per golfer.

GREEN FEES:$32 on weekdays,$37 on weekends.**First Tee Off:**Dawn.**Tee Times:**See
(Non-resident)   above.

ARCHITECT: Robert Trent Jones
YEAR BUILT:1948
PRO: Mike Wade,PGA
SEASON: All year

DISCOUNTS: Early Bird,Twilight
CART FEES:$26,$19 for 9 .Pull carts $3.
SPIKE POLICY: Soft spikes required
AVAILABLE FOR TOURNAMENTS:yes
Contact: John Monteforte **Days:**Tues. only
min 15.

COURSE DESCRIPTION: This is a links style course with scenic views.There is water on
most of the course and a lot of wind.

FEATURES\FACILITIES:
DRIVING RANGE-yes
RESTAURANT-yes
LOUNGE-yes
LESSONS-yes
PRO SHOP-yes

BANQUET-yes
WOMEN'S LOCKERS-yes
MEN'S LOCKERS-yes
MEETING ROOM-yes
NEARBY LODGING-yes

PRACTICE AREA-yes
BAR-yes
RENTAL CLUBS-yes
CREDIT CARDS-yes
SNACK BAR-yes

DIRECTIONS:495 LIE to exit 38 (Meadowbrook Parkway).Proceed South to exit M-10
to Loop Parkway.Proceed west for 2 ½ miles to the course on the right.

NO LAYOUT AVAILABLE

MARINE PARK GC (PUBLIC)

Brooklyn,NY

Course

GOLF COURSE 718 338-7113
TEE TIMES 718 338-7149

HOLES	YARDS blue\white\red	PAR	RATING blue\white\red	SLOPE blue\white\red
18	6866\6609\5323	72	00.0\70.5\00.0	000\118\000

HOLES	1	2	3	4	5	6	7	8	9	TOTAL
PAR	5	4	4	4	3	4	4	3	4	35
YARDS	498	437	445	328	181	384	359	178	405	3215
(Blue)	513	447	465	335	186	399	379	183	415	3322

HOLES	10	11	12	13	14	15	16	17	18	TOTAL
PAR	5	4	4	3	5	4	4	3	5	37
YARDS	476	370	369	173	495	431	393	177	510	3394
(Blue)	491	381	392	178	516	459	415	182	530	3544

GREEN FEES:$18 on weekdays,$20 weekends.**First Tee Off:**Dawn.**Tee Times:**Call 7
(Resident)   days in advance.There is a $2 reservations fee per golfer.

GREEN FEES:$24 on weekdays,$26 on weekends.
(Non-resident)

ARCHITECT: Robert Trent Jones
YEAR BUILT:1964
PRO: Bob Palmieri
SEASON: All year

DISCOUNTS: Seniors and Twilight
CART FEES:$24.50/$25.50
SPIKE POLICY: Spikes or soft spikes
AVAILABLE FOR TOURNAMENTS:yes
CONTACT: John Annunziata **DAYS:**Mon-Fri,
call for details.

COURSE DESCRIPTION: This is a links style course,long and wide,with a lot of wind.

FEATURES\FACILITIES:

DRIVING RANGE-no
RESTAURANT-yes
LOUNGE-no
LESSONS-yes
PRO SHOP-yes

BANQUET-yes
WOMEN'S LOCKERS-no
MEN'S LOCKERS-yes
MEETING ROOM-yes
NEARBY LODGING-no

PRACTICE AREA-yes
BAR-yes
RENTAL CLUBS-yes
CREDIT CARDS-yes
SNACK BAR-yes

DIRECTIONS: Belt Parkway to exit 11N.Proceed to second traffic light and make a left
into course.

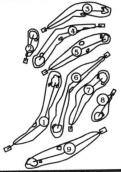

LONG ISLAND GOLF CONNECTION

MERRICK ROAD PARK GC
Merrick,NY   (PUBLIC)

GOLF COURSE 516 868-4650
TEE TIMES 516 868-4610

Course

HOLES	YARDS blue\white\red	PAR	RATING blue\white\red	SLOPE blue\white\red
9	0000\3115\2845	36	00.0\69.6\00.0	000\108\000

HOLES	1	2	3	4	5	6	7	8	9	TOTAL
PAR	5	3	4	4	4	5	4	3	4	36
YARDS	480	147	351	405	353	487	330	159	403	3115
(Blue)	000	000	000	000	000	000	000	000	000	0000

HOLES	10	11	12	13	14	15	16	17	18	TOTAL
PAR	0	0	0	0	0	0	0	0	0	00
YARDS	000	000	000	000	000	000	000	000	000	0000
(Blue)	000	000	000	000	000	000	000	000	000	0000

GREEN FEES:$8 on weekdays,$8 weekends.**First Tee Off:**6am.**Tee Times:**First come,
(Residents)   first serve.Course is closed on Wednesdays.

GREEN FEES:$10 on weekdays,$10 on weekends.There is a $12 guest fee at all times.
(Non-resident)   Non-residents must be accompanied by a resident.

ARCHITECT: Scheiner&Swit
YEAR BUILT:1965
PRO: Sam Musacchio
SEASON: All year

DISCOUNTS: Seniors
CART FEES: Pull carts only
SPIKE POLICY: Spikes or soft spikes
AVAILABLE FOR TOURNAMENTS:no

COURSE DESCRIPTION: This is a flat regulation sized 9 hole course.

FEATURES\FACILITIES:
DRIVING RANGE-yes
RESTAURANT-yes
LOUNGE-yes
LESSONS-yes
PRO SHOP-yes

BANQUET-yes
WOMEN'S LOCKERS-no
MEN'S LOCKERS-no
MEETING ROOM-yes
NEARBY LODGING-yes

PRACTICE AREA-yes
BAR-yes
RENTAL CLUBS-yes
CREDIT CARDS-yes
SNACK BAR-yes

DIRECTIONS:495 LIE to Meadowbrook Parkway South.Proceed to exit M-9,(Merrick Rd).
First traffic light make a right to course.

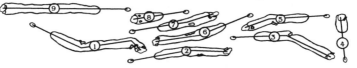

Oak Tree

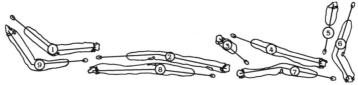

Dogwood

MIDDLE ISLAND CC

Middle Island,NY   (SEMI-PRIVATE)

Dogwood\Oak Tree

GOLF COURSE 516 924-5100

TEE TIMES 516 924-5100

HOLES	YARDS blue\white\red	PAR	RATING blue\white\red	SLOPE blue\white\red
18	6934\6542\5809	72	74.1\71.7\74.3	128\125\129

HOLES	1	2	3	4	5	6	7	8	9	TOTAL
PAR	4	5	3	4	3	4	4	5	4	36
YARDS	397	561	110	365	144	316	405	562	374	3234
(Blue)	430	584	128	384	175	340	438	589	393	3461

HOLES	10	11	12	13	14	15	16	17	18	TOTAL
PAR	5	4	4	3	4	4	4	3	5	36
YARDS	487	470	366	198	361	382	300	207	537	3308
(Blue)	511	484	389	209	370	397	323	227	563	3473

GREEN FEES:$25 on weekdays,$28 weekends.**First Tee Off:**6:30am on weekdays,1pm on weekends.Before 1pm reserved for members.**Tee Times:**There is a $25 fee (good for season) to reserve tee times 7 days in advance,or call 2 days in advance for a $5 extra charge per golfer.

ARCHITECT: Baier Lustgarten
YEAR BUILT:1965
PRO: Vinny Gallo,PGA
SEASON: All year

DISCOUNTS: None
CART FEES:$28 Pull carts $3
SPIKE POLICY: Soft spikes preferred
AVAILABLE FOR TOURNAMENTS:yes
CONTACT: Ryan Mulligan **DAYS:**Mon-Sun, min 16-max 220.

COURSE DESCRIPTION: Three 9 hole courses,all championship combination of 6600 yards.Designed by a professional landscaper.Dogwood and Oak Tree play tougher and tighter than Spruce which is the longest of the three.

FEATURES\FACILITIES:

DRIVING RANGE-yes
RESTAURANT-yes
LOUNGE-yes
LESSONS-yes
PRO SHOP-yes

BANQUET-yes
WOMEN'S LOCKERS-yes
MEN'S LOCKERS-yes
MEETING ROOM-yes
NEARBY LODGING-yes

PRACTICE AREA-yes
BAR-yes
RENTAL CLUBS-yes
CREDIT CARDS-yes
SNACK BAR-yes

DIRECTIONS:495 LIE to exit 66.Proceed north on Route 101,bear right at fork (Main St). Bear left at next fork (Middle Island\Yaphank Rd) to the course.

Spruce

Dogwood

MIDDLE ISLAND CC

Middle Island,NY   (SEMI-PRIVATE)

Dogwood\Spruce

GOLF COURSE 516 924-5100

TEE TIMES 516 924-5100

HOLES	YARDS blue\white\red	PAR	RATING blue\white\red	SLOPE blue\white\red
18	7015\6607\5909	72	74.1\71.7\74.3	128\125\129

HOLES	1	2	3	4	5	6	7	8	9	TOTAL
PAR	4	5	3	4	3	4	4	5	4	36
YARDS	397	561	110	365	144	316	405	562	374	3234
(Blue)	430	584	128	384	175	340	438	589	393	3461

HOLES	10	11	12	13	14	15	16	17	18	TOTAL
PAR	4	4	5	3	4	5	4	3	4	36
YARDS	449	345	529	189	389	530	393	157	392	3373
(Blue)	463	369	550	206	409	552	412	178	415	3554

GREEN FEES:$25 on weekdays,$28 weekends.**First Tee Off:**6:30am on weekdays,1pm on weekends.Before 1pm reserved for members.**Tee Times:**There is a $25 fee (good for season) to reserve tee times 7 days in advance,or call 2 days in advance for a $5 extra charge per golfer.

ARCHITECT: Baier Lustgarten
YEAR BUILT:1965
PRO: Vinny Gallo,PGA
SEASON: All year

DISCOUNTS: None
CART FEES:$28,Pull carts $3
SPIKE POLICY: Soft spikes preferred
AVAILABLE FOR TOURNAMENTS:yes
CONTACT: Ryan Mulligan **DAYS:**Mon-Sun, min 16-max 220.

COURSE DESCRIPTION: Three 9 hole courses,all championship combination of 6600 yards.Designed by a professional landscaper.Dogwood and Oak Tree play tougher and tighter than Spruce which is the longest of the three.

FEATURES\FACILITIES:

DRIVING RANGE-yes	BANQUET-yes	PRACTICE AREA-yes
RESTAURANT-yes	WOMEN'S LOCKERS-yes	BAR-yes
LOUNGE-yes	MEN'S LOCKERS-yes	RENTAL CLUBS-yes
LESSONS-yes	MEETING ROOM-yes	CREDIT CARDS-yes
PRO SHOP-yes	NEARBY LODGING-yes	SNACK BAR-yes

DIRECTIONS:495 LIE to exit 66.Proceed north on Route 101,bear right at fork (Main St). Bear left at next fork (Middle Island\Yaphank Rd) to the course.

Spruce

Oak Tree

MIDDLE ISLAND CC
Middle Island,NY   (SEMI-PRIVATE)
Oak Tree\Spruce

GOLF COURSE 516 924-5100
TEE TIMES 516 924-5100

HOLES	YARDS blue\white\red	PAR	RATING blue\white\red	SLOPE blue\white\red
18	7027\6681\5906	72	74.1\71.7\74.3	128\125\129

HOLES	1	2	3	4	5	6	7	8	9	TOTAL
PAR	5	4	4	3	4	4	4	3	5	36
YARDS	487	470	366	198	361	382	300	207	537	3308
(Blue)	511	484	389	209	370	397	323	227	563	3473

HOLES	10	11	12	13	14	15	16	17	18	TOTAL
PAR	4	4	5	3	4	5	4	3	4	36
YARDS	449	345	529	189	389	530	393	157	392	3373
(Blue)	463	369	550	206	409	552	412	178	415	3554

GREEN FEES:$25 on weekdays,$28 weekends.**First Tee Off:**6:30am on weekdays,1pm on weekends.Before 1pm reserved for members.**Tee Times:**There is a $25 fee (good for season) to reserve tee times 7 days in advance,or call 2 days in advance for a $5 extra charge per golfer.

ARCHITECT: Baier Lustgarten
YEAR BUILT:1965
PRO: Vinny Gallo,PGA
SEASON: All year

DISCOUNTS: None
CART FEES:$28,Pull carts $3
SPIKE POLICY: Soft spikes preferred
AVAILABLE FOR TOURNAMENTS:yes
CONTACT: Ryan Mulligan **DAYS:**Mon-Sun, min 16-max 220.

COURSE DESCRIPTION: Three 9 hole courses,all championship combination of 6600 yards.Designed by a professional landscaper.Dogwood and Oak Tree play tougher and tighter than Spruce which is the longest of the three.

FEATURES\FACILITIES:

DRIVING RANGE-yes	BANQUET-yes	PRACTICE AREA-yes
RESTAURANT-yes	WOMEN'S LOCKERS-yes	BAR-yes
LOUNGE-yes	MEN'S LOCKERS-yes	RENTAL CLUBS-yes
LESSONS-yes	MEETING ROOM-yes	CREDIT CARDS-yes
PRO SHOP-yes	NEARBY LODGING-yes	SNACK BAR-yes

DIRECTIONS:495 LIE to exit 66.Proceed north on Route 101,bear right at fork (Main St). Bear left at next fork (Middle Island\Yaphank Rd) to the course.

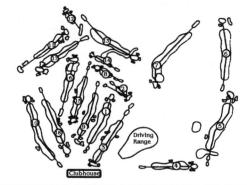

MONTAUK DOWNS STATE PARK

Montauk,NY (PUBLIC)

GOLF COURSE 516 668-5000
TEE TIMES 516 668-1234

Course

HOLES	YARDS blue\white\red	PAR	RATING blue\white\red	SLOPE blue\white\red
18	6762\6289\5797	72	73.3\71.2\74.2	135\130\132

HOLES	1	2	3	4	5	6	7	8	9	TOTAL
PAR	4	3	4	4	5	4	5	3	4	36
YARDS	372	115	374	396	488	326	490	154	435	3150
(Blue)	394	152	421	423	530	347	508	167	452	33940

HOLES	10	11	12	13	14	15	16	17	18	TOTAL
PAR	5	4	3	5	3	4	4	4	4	36
YARDS	464	289	179	474	185	407	362	362	417	3139
(Blue)	499	319	213	494	199	436	377	390	441	3368

GREEN FEES:$25 on weekdays,$30 weekends.**First Tee Off:**Dawn**Tee Times:**Call 7 days in advance with a photo ID card.Cards can be purchased at Montauk Downs,Sunken Meadow or Bethpage.The card cost is $25 and is valid for 3 years.There is a $3 reservation fee per golfer.

ARCHITECT: Robert Trent Jones
YEAR BUILT:1968
PRO: Kevin Smith,PGA
SEASON: All year

DISCOUNTS: Seniors,Twilight
CART FEES:$12.50 pp. Pull carts $2.50
SPIKE POLICY: Soft spikes preferred
AVAILABLE FOR TOURNAMENTS:yes
CONTACT: Tom Dess **DAYS:**Call for details.

COURSE DESCRIPTION: This course has been rated one of the best public courses in the country.The greens are small and well bunkered,constant wind makes club selection difficult.

FEATURES\FACILITIES:
DRIVING RANGE-yes
RESTAURANT-yes
LOUNGE-yes
LESSONS-yes
PRO SHOP-yes

BANQUET-yes
WOMEN'S LOCKERS-yes
MEN'S LOCKERS-yes
MEETING ROOM-yes
NEARBY LODGING-yes

PRACTICE AREA-yes
BAR-yes
RENTAL CLUBS-yes
CREDIT CARDS-yes
SNACK BAR-yes

DIRECTIONS:495 LIE to exit 70 and make a right onto County Route 111 South.Proceed to the end and make a left onto 27 East.Proceed to village of Montauk.Make a left on West Lake Drive.Proceed ¼ mile to Fairview and make a left to course.

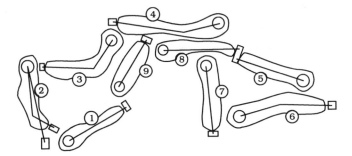

NORTHPORT VETERANS HOSPITAL GOLF COURSE 516 261-8000
Northport,NY (PUBLIC)

Course

HOLES	YARDS blue\white\red	PAR	RATING blue\white\red	SLOPE blue\white\red
9	0000\2347\0000	34	00.0\00.0\00.0	000\000\000

HOLES	1	2	3	4	5	6	7	8	9	TOTAL
PAR	4	3	4	5	4	4	3	4	3	34
YARDS	245	205	240	422	134	370	145	240	140	2347
(Blue)	000	000	000	000	000	000	000	000	000	0000

HOLES	10	11	12	13	14	15	16	17	18	TOTAL
PAR	0	0	0	0	0	0	0	0	0	00
YARDS	000	000	000	000	000	000	000	000	000	0000
(Blue)	000	000	000	000	000	000	000	000	000	0000

GREEN FEES:$9 on weekdays,$11 weekends.**First Tee Off:**Dawn.**Tee Times:**Same day only for reservations.Veterans pay $4 anytime.

GREEN FEES:$16 on weekdays,$18 on weekends.
(Non-resident)

ARCHITECT:N\A
YEAR BUILT:N\A
PRO: None
SEASON: March-December

DISCOUNTS: Seniors,Hospital employees
CART FEES: Pull carts $2.
SPIKE POLICY: Spikes or soft spikes
AVAILABLE FOR TOURNAMENTS:yes
Call for details.

COURSE DESCRIPTION:9 hole executive course with a few hills.Excellent for beginners.

FEATURES\FACILITIES:
DRIVING RANGE-no
RESTAURANT-no
LOUNGE-no
LESSONS-no
PRO SHOP-no

BANQUET-no
WOMEN'S LOCKERS-no
MEN'S LOCKERS-no
MEETING ROOM-no
NEARBY LODGING-no

PRACTICE AREA-no
BAR-no
RENTAL CLUBS-no
CREDIT CARDS-no
SNACK BAR-yes

DIRECTIONS:495 LIE to exit 53. (Sunken Meadow Parkway) North.Proceed to Route 25A West.Proceed West on Route 25A to Rinaldo Rd and make a left.Follow signs to Veterans Hospital and course.

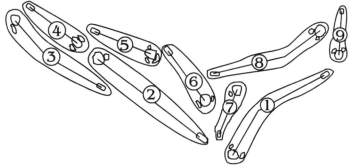

NORTH WOODMERE PARK GC

North Woodmere,NY   (PUBLIC)

GOLF COURSE 516 571-7814
PRO SHOP 516 791-8100

Executive Course

HOLES	YARDS blue\white\red	PAR	RATING blue\white\red	SLOPE blue\white\red
9	0000\2282\0000	31	00.0\00.0\00.0	000\000\000

HOLES	1	2	3	4	5	6	7	8	9	TOTAL
PAR	4	4	4	3	3	3	3	4	3	31
YARDS	390	395	310	177	167	200	143	360	140	2282
(Blue)	000	000	000	000	000	000	000	000	000	0000

HOLES	10	11	12	13	14	15	16	17	18	TOTAL
PAR	0	0	0	0	0	0	0	0	0	00
YARDS	000	000	000	000	000	000	000	000	000	0000
(Blue)	000	000	000	000	000	000	000	000	000	0000

GREEN FEES:$8 on weekdays,$9 weekends.**First Tee Off:**6am.
(Residents)   Residents must have leisure pass.Course is closed on Thursdays.

GREEN FEES:$16 on weekdays,$18 on weekends.
(Non-resident)

ARCHITECT:N\A
YEAR BUILT:1973
PRO: Tom Berry
SEASON: All year

DISCOUNTS: Seniors,Handicap,Volunteer
Firefighters (with leisure pass)
CART FEES: Pull carts $2
SPIKE POLICY: Spikes or soft spikes
AVAILABLE FOR TOURNAMENTS:no

COURSE DESCRIPTION: Flat 9 hole executive course.Extended tees for 1998.

FEATURES\FACILITIES:

DRIVING RANGE-yes
RESTAURANT-no
LOUNGE-yes
LESSONS-yes
PRO SHOP-yes

BANQUET-no
WOMEN'S LOCKERS-no
MEN'S LOCKERS-no
MEETING ROOM-no
NEARBY LODGING-no

PRACTICE AREA-yes
BAR-no
RENTAL CLUBS-yes
CREDIT CARDS-no
SNACK BAR-no

DIRECTIONS: Southern State Parkway to exit 17 South.Make a right.Bear left onto
Ocean Ave and proceed to Peninsula Blvd.Make a right and proceed 5 ½ miles to Branch
Blvd and make a right.Proceed 1 mile course is on the left.

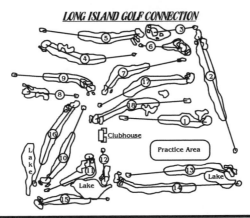

OYSTER BAY GC (SEMI-PRIVATE)   GOLF COURSE 516 677-5960

Woodbury,NY

Course

HOLES	YARDS blue\white\red	PAR	RATING blue\white\red	SLOPE blue\white\red
18	6351\5795\5109	70	71.5\69.0\68.7	131\126\119

HOLES	1	2	3	4	5	6	7	8	9	TOTAL
PAR	4	5	3	4	4	3	4	3	4	34
YARDS	295	531	130	375	354	147	354	207	281	2692
(Blue)	348	571	152	415	378	173	387	228	320	2972

HOLES	10	11	12	13	14	15	16	17	18	TOTAL
PAR	4	4	3	4	5	4	4	4	4	36
YARDS	334	250	118	358	470	344	412	426	391	3103
(Blue)	365	280	125	394	522	366	439	445	443	3379

GREEN FEES:$15 on weekdays,$22 weekends.**First Tee Off:**6am.**Tee Times:**First
(Resident)   come,first serve.Membership fee for residents $150.00.Discount rates for
(member)   resident Seniors,Volunteer Firefighters,and Auxiliary Police.Course is
                closed on Mondays.

GREEN FEES:$50 on weekdays,$62 on weekends.Membership fee for non-residents
(Non-resident) $300.00.Green fees for non-resident members are $30 on weekdays,$44
                on weekends.

ARCHITECT: Tom Fazio   **DISCOUNTS:**See above for membership discounts
YEAR BUILT:1989   **CART FEES:**$22 for resident members.
PRO: Bobby Basilico,PGA   **SPIKE POLICY:**Soft spikes required
SEASON: All year   **AVAILABLE FOR TOURNAMENTS:**yes
                                           CONTACT: Cory Comerford **DAYS:**Tues,Weds,Thurs,
                                           30-40 golfers.

COURSE DESCRIPTION: This is a very challenging course with tight fairways and elevated
greens that are well bunkered.Entire Clubhouse and Pro Shop remodeled.

FEATURES\FACILITIES:
DRIVING RANGE-yes   BANQUET-yes   PRACTICE AREA-yes
RESTAURANT-yes   WOMEN'S LOCKERS-yes   BAR-yes
LOUNGE-yes   MEN'S LOCKERS-yes   RENTAL CLUBS-yes
LESSONS-yes   MEETING ROOM-yes   CREDIT CARDS-no
PRO SHOP-yes   NEARBY LODGING-yes   SNACK BAR-yes

DIRECTIONS:495 LIE to exit 44N (Seaford Oyster Bay Expressway).Proceed to exit 14E.
Proceed on Route 25 to Southwoods Rd and make a left to course on the left.

NO LAYOUT AVAILABLE

PENINSULA GC   (SEMI-PRIVATE)   GOLF COURSE 516 498-9779
Massepequa,NY

Course

HOLES	YARDS blue\white\red	PAR	RATING blue\white\red	SLOPE blue\white\red
9	0000\3291\0000	37	00.0\71.5\00.0	000\123\000

HOLES	1	2	3	4	5	6	7	8	9	TOTAL
PAR	5	4	4	4	4	3	4	4	5	37
YARDS	460	442	292	334	410	160	383	350	460	3291
(Blue)	000	000	000	000	000	000	000	000	000	0000

HOLES	10	11	12	13	14	15	16	17	18	TOTAL
PAR	0	0	0	0	0	0	0	0	0	00
YARDS	000	000	000	000	000	000	000	000	000	0000
(Blue)	000	000	000	000	000	000	000	000	000	0000

GREEN FEES:$11 on weekdays,$12 weekends.**First Tee Off:**6am;Sundays 12:30pm. **Tee Times:**First come,first serve.Play twice for additional $8.Course is closed to non-members Sundays until 12:30pm.

ARCHITECT:N\A
YEAR BUILT:1920'S
PRO: George Tavalaro,PGA
SEASON: All year

DISCOUNTS: None
CART FEES:$12 1st 9,$10 for 2nd 9
SPIKE POLICY: Soft spikes required
AVAILABLE FOR TOURNAMENTS:yes
CONTACT: Larry Maglione for details.

COURSE DESCRIPTION: This 9 hole executive course is flat,long and wide open.

FEATURES\FACILITIES:

DRIVING RANGE-no
RESTAURANT-yes
LOUNGE-yes
LESSONS-yes
PRO SHOP-yes

BANQUET-no
WOMEN'S LOCKERS-no
MEN'S LOCKERS-yes
MEETING ROOM-yes
NEARBY LODGING-no

PRACTICE AREA-yes
BAR-yes
RENTAL CLUBS-yes
CREDIT CARDS-no
SNACK BAR-yes

DIRECTIONS:495 LIE to exit 44S (Seaford Oyster Bay Expressway).Exit at Merrick Rd and make a left.Proceed to Unqua Rd and make a right.Proceed to course at the end of the road.

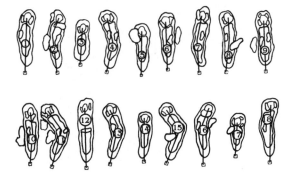

PINE HILLS CC   (SEMI-PRIVATE)
Manorville,NY

Course

GOLF COURSE 516 878-4343
TEE TIMES 615 878-7103

HOLES	YARDS blue\white\red	PAR	RATING blue\white\red	SLOPE blue\white\red
18	7030\6443\5218	73	72.2\69.8\71.0	121\117\116

HOLES	1	2	3	4	5	6	7	8	9	TOTAL
PAR	4	5	3	4	4	4	4	5	4	37
YARDS	386	458	143	389	300	379	375	473	426	3329
(Blue)	400	488	176	402	335	428	451	539	450	3669

HOLES	10	11	12	13	14	15	16	17	18	TOTAL
PAR	4	4	5	4	3	5	4	3	4	36
YARDS	378	406	490	290	180	464	324	142	440	3114
(Blue)	393	429	504	305	220	498	396	160	456	3361

GREEN FEES:$25 on weekdays,$28 weekends.**First Tee Off:**6am.**Tee Times:**There is a $25 fee (good for season) to reserve tee times.Add $5 extra charge for 2 days in advance calling.Course is closed to non-members on Saturday until 2pm and Sunday until 1pm.

ARCHITECT: Roger Tooker
YEAR BUILT:1973
PRO: Jimmi Conway,PGA
SEASON: All year

DISCOUNTS: Seniors-after 12pm.
CART FEES:$28
SPIKE POLICY: Soft spikes required
AVAILABLE FOR TOURNAMENTS:yes
CONTACT: Peter **DAYS:**Mon-Fri,min 16-max 82.
Sundays start after 11:30pm.

COURSE DESCRIPTION: This is a fun course that appears easy,but hides some subtle breaks.Regarded by Golf Digest as the best maintained course on Long Island.

FEATURES\FACILITIES:

DRIVING RANGE-yes
RESTAURANT-yes
LOUNGE-yes
LESSONS-yes
PRO SHOP-yes

BANQUET-no
WOMEN'S LOCKERS-yes
MEN'S LOCKERS-yes
MEETING ROOM-no
NEARBY LODGING-yes

PRACTICE AREA-yes
BAR-yes
RENTAL CLUBS-yes
CREDIT CARDS-yes
SNACK BAR-yes

DIRECTIONS:495 LIE to exit 69.The course is 1 mile south on Wading River Rd on the right.

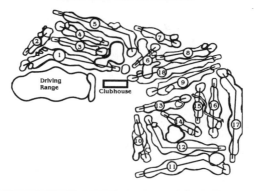

PONDS AT LAKE GROVE GC
Lake Grove,NY   (PUBLIC)
Executive Course

GOLF COURSE 516 737-4649
TEE TIMES 516 737-9109

HOLES	YARDS blue\white\red	PAR	RATING blue\white\red	SLOPE blue\white\red
18	0000\3107\0000	60	00.0\56.9\00.0	000\088\000

HOLES	1	2	3	4	5	6	7	8	9	TOTAL
PAR	4	3	3	3	4	3	3	3	3	29
YARDS	259	101	147	141	259	98	124	152	183	1464
(Blue)	000	000	000	000	000	000	000	000	000	0000

HOLES	10	11	12	13	14	15	16	17	18	TOTAL
PAR	3	4	4	3	3	3	3	4	4	31
YARDS	133	264	241	145	118	86	137	264	255	1643
(Blue)	000	000	000	000	000	000	000	000	000	0000

GREEN FEES:$12 on weekdays,$15 weekends.**First Tee Off:**6am.**Tee Times:**Call 7
(Resident)   days in advance.

GREEN FEES:$16 on weekdays,$20 on weekends.
(Non-resident)

ARCHITECT: William Johnson
YEAR BUILT:1995
PRO: Directory of Teaching Pros
SEASON: All year

DISCOUNTS: Seniors and Twilight
CART FEES:$10 pp.Pull carts $3.25
SPIKE POLICY: Soft spikes required
AVAILABLE FOR TOURNAMENTS:yes
CONTACT: Susan Crean **DAYS:**Mon-Fri,weekend
starts after 1pm.Number of golfers 60.

COURSE DESCRIPTION: Pristine condition featuring 12 par 3's and 6 par 4's.Water
comes into play on 6 holes and the greens are quick.New for 1998 3-tier heated and
enclosed driving range,miniature golf and a new Pro Sop.

FEATURES\FACILITIES:

DRIVING RANGE-yes	BANQUET-no	PRACTICE AREA-yes
RESTAURANT-yes	WOMEN'S LOCKERS-no	BAR-yes
LOUNGE-yes	MEN'S LOCKERS-no	RENTAL CLUBS-yes
LESSONS-yes	MEETING ROOM-yes	CREDIT CARDS-yes
PRO SHOP-yes	NEARBY LODGING-yes	SNACK BAR-yes

DIRECTIONS:495 LIE to exit 62 North to Route 347.Proceed West for approx. 2 miles to
New Moriches Rd and make a left.Course is on the left.

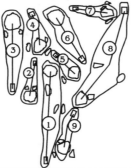

LONG ISLAND GOLF CONNECTION

POXABOGUE GC (PUBLIC) GOLF COURSE 516 537-0025
Bridgehampton,NY

Executive Course

HOLES	YARDS blue\white\red	PAR	RATING blue\white\red	SLOPE blue\white\red
9	0000\1706\0000	30	00.0\00.0\00.0	000\000\000

HOLES	1	2	3	4	5	6	7	8	9	TOTAL
PAR	4	3	4	3	3	3	3	4	3	30
YARDS	322	135	317	137	63	175	79	320	160	1706
(Blue)	000	000	000	000	000	000	000	000	000	0000

HOLES	10	11	12	13	14	15	16	17	18	TOTAL
PAR	0	0	0	0	0	0	0	0	0	00
YARDS	000	000	000	000	000	000	000	000	000	0000
(Blue)	000	000	000	000	000	000	000	000	000	0000

GREEN FEES:$9 on weekdays,$11 weekends.**First Tee Off:**7am.**Tee Times:**First come, first serve.Play second round for half price.

ARCHITECT: Liberty&Tredwell
YEAR BUILT:1962
PRO: Bob Vishno,PGA
SEASON: March-December

DISCOUNTS: Ten round card is available for $80 weekdays,$90 weekends.
CART FEES: Pull carts $2.50
SPIKE POLICY: Spikes or soft spikes
AVAILABLE FOR TOURNAMENTS:yes
CONTACT: Rich Walker **DAYS:**Mon-Sun,min 15-max 40 golfers.

COURSE DESCRIPTION:9 hole executive course with a few hills.Excellent for beginners. New tee boxes added for 1998.

FEATURES\FACILITIES:

DRIVING RANGE-yes
RESTAURANT-yes
LOUNGE-no
LESSONS-yes
PRO SHOP-yes

BANQUET-no
WOMEN'S LOCKERS-no
MEN'S LOCKERS-no
MEETING ROOM-no
NEARBY LODGING-yes

PRACTICE AREA-yes
BAR-no
RENTAL CLUBS-yes
CREDIT CARDS-no
SNACK BAR-yes

DIRECTIONS:495 LIE to exit 70.Make a right.Proceed to the end and make a left onto Route 27.Proceed into the Town of Bridgehampton and at the Cadillac Dealer make a left onto Montauk Hwy.Proceed East for 6 ½ miles to the course on the left.

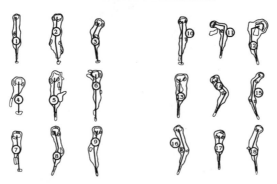

ROCK HILL GC (SEMI-PRIVATE)
Manorville,NY
Course

GOLF COURSE 516 878-2250
TEE TIMES 516 878-2250

HOLES	YARDS blue\white\red	PAR	RATING blue\white\red	SLOPE blue\white\red
18	7050\6465\5390	71	73.4\70.7\71.4	131\126\121

HOLES	1	2	3	4	5	6	7	8	9	TOTAL
PAR	4	5	4	3	4	4	3	4	4	35
YARDS	375	530	330	160	360	360	150	365	405	3035
(Blue)	415	555	350	200	420	390	180	390	435	3335

HOLES	10	11	12	13	14	15	16	17	18	TOTAL
PAR	4	4	5	3	4	5	4	3	4	36
YARDS	425	360	535	165	365	550	435	170	425	3430
(Blue)	455	390	570	195	390	585	475	205	450	3715

GREEN FEES:$26 on weekdays,$30 weekends.**First Tee Off:**7am/6am.**Tee Times:**Call 7 days in advance.There is a $6 reservation fee per golfer.Carts are mandatory with tee times and on weekends.Course is closed to non-members on weekends until 11am.

ARCHITECT: Frank Duanne
YEAR BUILT:1964
PRO: George Cosgrove,PGA
SEASON: All year

DISCOUNTS: Twilight,Seniors
CART FEES:$28
SPIKE POLICY: Spikes or soft spikes
AVAILABLE FOR TOURNAMENTS:yes
CONTACT: Bob Becker **DAYS:**Mon-Sun, min 24-max 144.

COURSE DESCRIPTION: The front 9 on this course provides short,hilly,tree-lined fairways,while the back 9 is wide open and long.

FEATURES\FACILITIES:

DRIVING RANGE-yes	BANQUET-yes	PRACTICE AREA-yes
RESTAURANT-yes	WOMEN'S LOCKERS-yes	BAR-yes
LOUNGE-yes	MEN'S LOCKERS-yes	RENTAL CLUBS-yes
LESSONS-yes	MEETING ROOM-yes	CREDIT CARDS-yes
PRO SHOP-yes	NEARBY LODGING-yes	SNACK BAR-yes

DIRECTIONS:495 LIE to exit 70.Make a right and proceed to the first traffic light (Chapman Blvd) and make a right.Proceed 1 ½ mile to Clancy Rd and make a left.Proceed to course on the left.

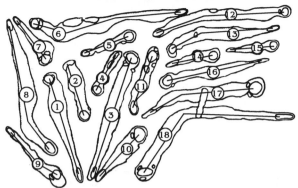

ROLLING OAKS GC   (PUBLIC)

Rocky Point,NY
Course

GOLF COURSE 516 744-3200
TEE TIMES 516 744-3200

HOLES	YARDS blue\white\red	PAR	RATING blue\white\red	SLOPE blue\white\red
18	4738\4348\3608	65	00.0\62.9\67.0	000\110\111

HOLES	1	2	3	4	5	6	7	8	9	TOTAL
PAR	4	3	4	3	3	5	3	4	3	32
YARDS	278	156	319	109	153	408	144	355	180	2102
(Blue)	305	160	335	115	160	470	150	375	185	2255

HOLES	10	11	12	13	14	15	16	17	18	TOTAL
PAR	3	3	4	4	3	3	4	4	5	33
YARDS	150	161	366	283	129	138	266	308	445	2246
(Blue)	160	175	420	320	130	148	310	345	475	2483

GREEN FEES:$22 on weekdays,$25 weekends.**First Tee Off:**Dawn.**Tee Times:**Call 7 days prior.There is a $3 fee per golfer for weekend reservations;no fee for weekday reservations.Seniors can buy pass for weekday unlimited golf.

ARCHITECT: Pete Colacci
YEAR BUILT:N\A
PRO: Jim Haughey,PGA
SEASON: All year

DISCOUNTS: Seniors and Twilight
CART FEES:$28,Single $16.Pull carts $5.
SPIKE POLICY: Spike or soft spikes
AVAILABLE FOR TOURNAMENTS:yes
CONTACT: Jim Haughey **DAYS:**Mon-Sun,weekend start after 10am.Shotgun starts min 80,max 144.

COURSE DESCRIPTION: Toughest 18 little holes in the business.Tree-lined,well bunkered course with small greens.

FEATURES\FACILITIES:

DRIVING RANGE-no
RESTAURANT-yes
LOUNGE-yes
LESSONS-yes
PRO SHOP-yes

BANQUET-yes
WOMEN'S LOCKERS-no
MEN'S LOCKERS-no
MEETING ROOM-no
NEARBY LODGING-yes

PRACTICE AREA-yes
BAR-yes
RENTAL CLUBS-yes
CREDIT CARDS-yes
SNACK BAR-yes

DIRECTIONS:495 LIE to exit 63 North.Proceed to Route 25A and make a right.Course is 4 miles on the left.

NO LAYOUT AVAILABLE

SAG HARBOR GC (PUBLIC) GOLF COURSE 516 725-2503
Sag Harbor,NY

Course

HOLES	YARDS blue\white\red	PAR	RATING blue\white\red	SLOPE blue\white\red
9	0000\2619\0000	35	00.0\00.0\00.0	000\000\000

HOLES	1	2	3	4	5	6	7	8	9	TOTAL
PAR	4	4	3	4	4	4	5	3	4	35
YARDS	321	310	145	274	291	341	394	191	352	2619
(Blue)	000	000	000	000	000	000	000	000	000	0000

HOLES	10	11	12	13	14	15	16	17	18	TOTAL
PAR	0	0	0	0	0	0	0	0	0	00
YARDS	000	000	000	000	000	000	000	000	000	0000
(Blue)	000	000	000	000	000	000	000	000	000	0000

GREEN FEES:$10 on weekdays,$15 weekends.**First Tee Off:**7am.**Tee Times:**First come,first serve.Price includes unlimited play.

ARCHITECT:N\A
YEAR BUILT:1910
PRO: None
SEASON: All year

DISCOUNTS: Unlimited play
CART FEES: Pull carts $3
SPIKE POLICY: Soft spikes required
AVAILABLE FOR TOURNAMENTS:no

COURSE DESCRIPTION: This links style course is wide open.

FEATURES\FACILITIES:

DRIVING RANGE-no
RESTAURANT-no
LOUNGE-no
LESSONS-no
PRO SHOP-no

BANQUET-no
WOMEN'S LOCKERS-no
MEN'S LOCKERS-no
MEETING ROOM-no
NEARBY LODGING-yes

PRACTICE AREA-yes
BAR-yes,beer only
RENTAL CLUBS-yes
CREDIT CARDS-no
SNACK BAR-yes

DIRECTIONS:495 LIE to exit 70.Make a right onto Route 101 South.Proceed to the end and make a left onto 27 East.Proceed to the end and make a left onto Montauk Hwy. Proceed to Route 114 and make a left.Follow signs to course on the right.

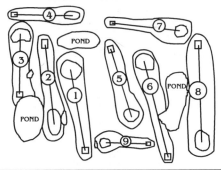

SANDY POND GC (PUBLIC)

Riverhead,NY

GOLF COURSE 516 727-0909

Course

HOLES	YARDS blue\white\red	PAR	RATING blue\white\red	SLOPE blue\white\red
9	0000\1070\0935	27	00.0\00.0\00.0	000\000\000

HOLES	1	2	3	4	5	6	7	8	9	TOTAL
PAR	3	3	3	3	3	3	3	3	3	27
YARDS	105	110	120	85	120	160	120	160	90	1070
(Blue)	000	000	000	000	000	000	000	000	000	0000

HOLES	10	11	12	13	14	15	16	17	18	TOTAL
PAR	0	0	0	0	0	0	0	0	0	00
YARDS	000	000	000	000	000	000	000	000	000	0000
(Blue)	000	000	000	000	000	000	000	000	000	0000

GREEN FEES:$5 on weekdays,$6 weekends.**First Tee Off:**Dawn.**Tee Times:**First come, first serve.Members pay one price for unlimited play for the season.

ARCHITECT:N\A
YEAR BUILT:1970
PRO: Lessons Instructor
SEASON: All year

DISCOUNTS: Seniors
CART FEES: Pull carts $1
SPIKE POLICY: Spikes or soft spikes
AVAILABLE FOR TOURNAMENTS:no

COURSE DESCRIPTION: This is a pitch and putt course with open fairways.Excellent course to help improve on your short game.

FEATURES\FACILITIES:

DRIVING RANGE-no
RESTAURANT-no
LOUNGE-no
LESSONS-yes
PRO SHOP-no

BANQUET-no
WOMEN'S LOCKERS-no
MEN'S LOCKERS-no
MEETING ROOM-no
NEARBY LODGING-no

PRACTICE AREA-yes
BAR-no
RENTAL CLUBS-yes
CREDIT CARDS-no
SNACK BAR-no

DIRECTIONS:495 LIE to the last exit.Proceed 2 miles to the traffic circle and proceed North on Roanoke Ave approx. ½ mile to the course on the left.

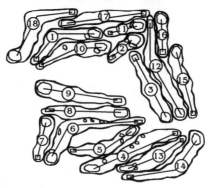

SMITHTOWN LANDING GC

Smithtown,NY   (SEMI-PRIVATE)

GOLF COURSE 516 360-7618

Course

HOLES	YARDS blue\white\red	PAR	RATING blue\white\red	SLOPE blue\white\red
18	6114\5858\5263	72	69.4\68.3\70.1	129\127\126

HOLES	1	2	3	4	5	6	7	8	9	TOTAL
PAR	4	3	4	5	4	5	3	4	4	36
YARDS	352	145	260	580	357	450	160	300	360	2964
(Blue)	362	155	275	590	370	465	165	320	370	3072

HOLES	10	11	12	13	14	15	16	17	18	TOTAL
PAR	4	3	5	4	5	4	3	4	4	36
YARDS	273	145	469	362	465	320	180	320	360	2894
(Blue)	293	155	485	374	475	330	190	350	390	3072

GREEN FEES:$18 on weekdays,$20 weekends.**First Tee Off:**6:30am.**Tee Times:**Call
(Residents)   7 days in advance for weekend.During the week first come,first serve.
The course is closed on Mondays.Residents must have resident permit.
Call permit office for details 516 360-7617.

GREEN FEES:$26 on weekdays,$27 on weekends.Course is closed to non-residents
(Non-resident)   on weekends,unless accompanied by Town resident.**Tee Times:**See above.

ARCHITECT:N\A
YEAR BUILT:1961
PRO: Mike Hebron,PGA
SEASON: All year

DISCOUNTS: Seniors,Juniors on weekdays only
CART FEES:$24,Pull carts $3
SPIKE POLICY: Soft spikes preferred
AVAILABLE FOR TOURNAMENTS:yes
CONTACT: Douglas or Chris **DAYS:**Wed&Thurs,
Mon for 80 or more golfers.

COURSE DESCRIPTION: This course has a private club atmosphere.Scenic and well
maintained.The fairways are tight and the greens are small and well bunkered.

FEATURES\FACILITIES:
DRIVING RANGE-yes
RESTAURANT-yes
LOUNGE-yes
LESSONS-yes
PRO SHOP-yes

BANQUET-yes
WOMEN'S LOCKERS-no
MEN'S LOCKERS-no
MEETING ROOM-yes
NEARBY LODGING-yes

PRACTICE AREA-yes
BAR-yes
RENTAL CLUBS-no
CREDIT CARDS-no
SNACK BAR-yes

DIRECTIONS:495 LIE to exit 53 North (Sunken Meadow Parkway).Proceed to Route 25A
to fifth traffic light.Proceed straight onto Rose St ¼ mile to course.

INDIAN HEAD GOLF PARK
Fore Hundred Old Northport Rd.
Kings Park
269-4100
Mon-Fri 8am-11pm Sat-Sun 7am-11pm

World's Longest Synthetic Turf Tee-Line. No Mats!
No Cement Tee-Line!

		Target Greens		
Seniors	**Gift Certificates Available**		**Monday's Ladies Day**	25A — Indian Head Golf Park / Old Northport Rd. / Indian Head Rd.
Mon-Fri 8am-5pm $1.00 OFF			**$1.00 OFF**	

Just minutes From Smithtown Landing!!

SMITHTOWN LANDING GC

Smithtown,NY   (SEMI-PRIVATE)

GOLF COURSE 516 360-7618

Pitch and Putt

HOLES	YARDS blue\white\red	PAR	RATING blue\white\red	SLOPE blue\white\red
9	0000\1143\0000	27	00.0\00.0\00.0	000\000\000

HOLES	1	2	3	4	5	6	7	8	9	TOTAL
PAR	3	3	3	3	3	3	3	3	3	27
YARDS	150	90	125	110	165	153	140	90	120	1143
(Blue)	000	000	000	000	000	000	000	000	000	0000

HOLES	10	11	12	13	14	15	16	17	18	TOTAL
PAR	0	0	0	0	0	0	0	0	0	00
YARDS	000	000	000	000	000	000	000	000	000	0000
(Blue)	000	000	000	000	000	000	000	000	000	0000

GREEN FEES:$6.50 on weekdays,$7.50 weekends.**First Tee Off:**6:30am.**Tee Times:**First
(Residents)   come,first serve.Price includes unlimited play.The course is closed on
Mondays.Residents must have resident permit.Call permit office for details
516 360-7617.

GREEN FEES:$7.50 on weekdays,$9 on weekends.Course is closed to non-residents
(Non-resident)   on weekends,unless accompanied by Town resident.**Tee Times:**See above.

ARCHITECT:N\A
YEAR BUILT:1961
PRO: Mike Hebron,PGA
SEASON: All year

DISCOUNTS: Seniors,Juniors on weekdays only
CART FEES:$13.50,Pull carts $2.
SPIKE POLICY: Soft spikes preferred
AVAILABLE FOR TOURNAMENTS:yes
CONTACT: Douglas or Chris **DAYS:**Wed&Thurs,
Mon for 80 or more golfers.

COURSE DESCRIPTION: This course is tight and the greens are small.Great place to
practice your short game.

FEATURES\FACILITIES:

DRIVING RANGE-yes	BANQUET-yes	PRACTICE AREA-yes
RESTAURANT-yes	WOMEN'S LOCKERS-no	BAR-yes
LOUNGE-yes	MEN'S LOCKERS-no	RENTAL CLUBS-no
LESSONS-yes	MEETING ROOM-yes	CREDIT CARDS-no
PRO SHOP-yes	NEARBY LODGING-yes	SNACK BAR-yes

DIRECTIONS: 495 LIE to exit 53 North (Sunken Meadow Parkway).Proceed to Route 25A
to fifth traffic light.Proceed straight onto Rose St ¼ mile to course.

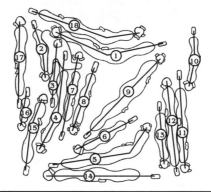

SPRING LAKE GC (PUBLIC)

Middle Island,NY

Thunderbird Course

GOLF COURSE 516 924-5115
TEE TIMES 516 924-5115

HOLES	YARDS blue\white\red	PAR	RATING blue\white\red	SLOPE blue\white\red
18	7048\6455\5732	72	73.2\70.5\70.0	128\123\120

HOLES	1	2	3	4	5	6	7	8	9	TOTAL
PAR	4	4	3	5	4	3	4	4	5	36
YARDS	436	340	180	507	339	154	420	381	504	3261
(Blue)	456	382	212	557	381	178	452	431	534	3583

HOLES	10	11	12	13	14	15	16	17	18	TOTAL
PAR	4	5	4	3	4	4	3	4	5	36
YARDS	315	500	340	173	410	333	155	427	541	3194
(Blue)	332	525	360	214	456	362	170	475	571	3465

GREEN FEES:$30 on weekdays,$34 weekends.**First Tee Off:**Dawn.**Tee Times:**Call 7 days in advance.Carts are mandatory with reservation and on weekends.

ARCHITECT: Charles Jurgens
YEAR BUILT:1967
PRO: Loring Hawkins,PGA
SEASON: All year

DISCOUNTS: Seniors and Twilight
CART FEES:$28,Pull carts $3
SPIKE POLICY: Soft spikes preferred
AVAILABLE FOR TOURNAMENTS:yes
CONTACT: Loring Hawkins **DAYS:**Mon-Sun, weekends start after 11am.Min 40,max 120 golfers.

COURSE DESCRIPTION: This course is long and challenging with large greens and three water holes.

FEATURES\FACILITIES:

DRIVING RANGE-yes
RESTAURANT-yes
LOUNGE-yes
LESSONS-yes
PRO SHOP-yes

BANQUET-yes
WOMEN'S LOCKERS-no
MEN'S LOCKERS-yes
MEETING ROOM-no
NEARBY LODGING-yes

PRACTICE AREA-yes
BAR-yes
RENTAL CLUBS-yes
CREDIT CARDS-no
SNACK BAR-yes

DIRECTIONS:495 LIE to exit 64.Proceed on Route 112 North to Middle Country Rd and make a right.Proceed 2 miles to the course on the right.

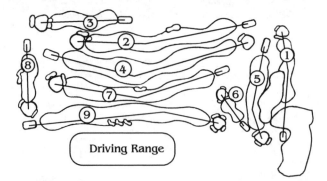

SPRING LAKE GC (PUBLIC)
Middle Island,NY
Sandpiper Course

GOLF COURSE 516 924-5115
TEE TIMES 516 924-5115

HOLES	YARDS			PAR	RATING			SLOPE
	blue\white\red				blue\white\red			blue\white\red
9	3250\3053\2607			36	00.0\69.4\00.0			000\125\000

HOLES	1	2	3	4	5	6	7	8	9	TOTAL
PAR	5	4	3	4	4	3	4	4	5	36
YARDS	483	348	190	485	335	102	314	332	491	3053
(Blue)	522	365	210	481	358	118	329	358	509	3250

HOLES	10	11	12	13	14	15	16	17	18	TOTAL
PAR	0	0	0	0	0	0	0	0	0	00
YARDS	000	000	000	000	000	000	000	000	000	0000
(Blue)	000	000	000	000	000	000	000	000	000	0000

GREEN FEES:$14 on weekdays,$16 weekends.**First Tee Off:**Dawn.**Tee Times:**Call 7
days in advance.Carts are mandatory with reservation and on weekends.

ARCHITECT: Charles Jurgens
YEAR BUILT:1967
PRO: Loring Hawkins,PGA
SEASON: All year

DISCOUNTS: Seniors and Twilight
CART FEES:$14,Pull carts $3
SPIKE POLICY: Soft spikes preferred
AVAILABLE FOR TOURNAMENTS:yes
CONTACT: Loring Hawkins **DAYS:**Mon-Sun,
weekends start after 11am.Min 40,max 120 golfers.

COURSE DESCRIPTION: The Sandpiper is a fun,challenging course.

FEATURES\FACILITIES:
DRIVING RANGE-yes
RESTAURANT-yes
LOUNGE-yes
LESSONS-yes
PRO SHOP-yes

BANQUET-yes
WOMEN'S LOCKERS-no
MEN'S LOCKERS-yes
MEETING ROOM-no
NEARBY LODGING-yes

PRACTICE AREA-yes
BAR-yes
RENTAL CLUBS-yes
CREDIT CARDS-no
SNACK BAR-yes

DIRECTIONS:495 LIE to exit 64.Proceed on Route 112 North to Middle Country Rd and
make a right.Proceed 2 miles to the course on the right.

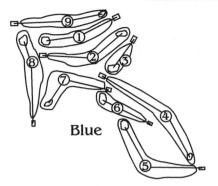

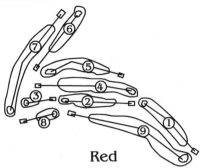

Blue

Red

SUNKEN MEADOW STATE PARK
Kings Park,NY   (PUBLIC)
Blue\Red

GOLF COURSE 516 269-3838
TEE TIMES 516 269-0707

HOLES	YARDS blue\white\red	PAR	RATING blue\white\red	SLOPE blue\white\red
18	0000\6100\0000	71	00.0\00.0\00.0	000\128\000

HOLES	1	2	3	4	5	6	7	8	9	TOTAL
PAR	4	4	3	5	4	3	4	4	4	35
YARDS	333	393	137	507	413	190	360	380	347	3060
(Blue)	000	000	000	000	000	000	000	000	000	0000

HOLES	10	11	12	13	14	15	16	17	18	TOTAL
PAR	4	4	3	4	4	4	5	3	5	36
YARDS	305	300	130	410	375	345	505	155	515	3040
(Blue)	000	000	000	000	000	000	000	000	000	0000

GREEN FEES:$18 on weekdays,$22 weekends.**First Tee Off:**6am.**Tee Times:**Call 7 days in advance with a photo ID card.Cards can be purchased at Sunken Meadow,Montauk Downs or Bethpage.The card cost is $25 and is valid for 3 years.There is a $3 reservation fee per golfer.

ARCHITECT: Alfred Tull
YEAR BUILT:1953
PRO: Kevin Smith,PGA
SEASON: April-December

DISCOUNTS: Seniors
CART FEES:$14 for 9,$24 for 18.
SPIKE POLICY: Soft spikes preferred
AVAILABLE FOR TOURNAMENTS:yes
CONTACT: Doug Molauder 516 269-4333
DAYS: Mon,Weds,Fri,only.Min 40,max 120.Start after 11am,no shotgun starts.

COURSE DESCRIPTION: In 1998 there will be one 18 hole course and one 9 hole course. The combination will rotate.On the blue course 7 out of the 9 holes are doglegs.The other 2 are par 3's.The red course is very hilly.

FEATURES\FACILITIES:
DRIVING RANGE-yes
RESTAURANT-yes
LOUNGE-yes
LESSONS-yes
PRO SHOP-yes

BANQUET-yes
WOMEN'S LOCKERS-no
MEN'S LOCKERS-no
MEETING ROOM-yes
NEARBY LODGING-yes

PRACTICE AREA-yes
BAR-yes
RENTAL CLUBS-yes
CREDIT CARDS-no
SNACK BAR-yes

DIRECTIONS:495 LIE to exit 53N (Sunken Meadow Parkway).Proceed North to the Park and the course.

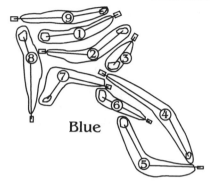

Blue

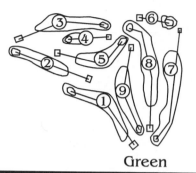

Green

SUNKEN MEADOW STATE PARK

Kings Park,NY   (PUBLIC)

Blue\Green

GOLF COURSE 516 269-3838

TEE TIMES 516 269-0707

HOLES	YARDS blue\white\red	PAR	RATING blue\white\red	SLOPE blue\white\red
18	0000\6185\0000	71	00.0\00.0\00.0	000\129\000

HOLES	1	2	3	4	5	6	7	8	9	TOTAL
PAR	4	4	3	5	4	3	4	4	4	35
YARDS	333	393	137	507	413	190	360	380	347	3060
(Blue)	000	000	000	000	000	000	000	000	000	0000

HOLES	10	11	12	13	14	15	16	17	18	TOTAL
PAR	4	4	4	3	4	3	5	5	4	36
YARDS	350	385	395	175	340	145	470	485	380	3125
(Blue)	000	000	000	000	000	000	000	000	000	0000

GREEN FEES:$18 on weekdays,$22 weekends.**First Tee Off:**6am.**Tee Times:**Call 7 days in advance with a photo ID card.Cards can be purchased at Sunken Meadow,Montauk Downs or Bethpage.The card cost is $25 and is valid for 3 years.There is a $3 reservation fee per golfer.

ARCHITECT: Alfred Tull
YEAR BUILT:1953
PRO: Kevin Smith,PGA
SEASON: April-December

DISCOUNTS: Seniors
CART FEES:$14 for 9,$24 for 18.
SPIKE POLICY: Soft spikes preferred
AVAILABLE FOR TOURNAMENTS:yes
CONTACT: Doug Molauder 516 269-4333
DAYS: Mon,Weds,Fri,only.Min 40,max 120.Start after 11am,no shotgun starts.

COURSE DESCRIPTION: In 1998 there will be one 18 hole course and one 9 hole course. The combination will rotate.On the blue course 7 out of the 9 holes are doglegs.The other 2 are par 3's.The green course is the easiest to score on,but the longest.

FEATURES\FACILITIES:

DRIVING RANGE-yes
RESTAURANT-yes
LOUNGE-yes
LESSONS-yes
PRO SHOP-yes

BANQUET-yes
WOMEN'S LOCKERS-no
MEN'S LOCKERS-no
MEETING ROOM-yes
NEARBY LODGING-yes

PRACTICE AREA-yes
BAR-yes
RENTAL CLUBS-yes
CREDIT CARDS-no
SNACK BAR-yes

DIRECTIONS:495 LIE to exit 53N (Sunken Meadow Parkway).Proceed North to the Park and the course.

What is the best value in GOLF?

For as little as pennies a shot,
YOU CAN WIN
a fantastic golf vacation at Wild Dunes, SC and a chance to win **ONE MILLION DOLLARS!** Here's how....

JOIN GOLF MARKETING'S

$Million Dollar Hole-In-One Club$

If you join the Club today, your next ace wins you a 3-day golf vacation at Wild Dunes, Charleston, South Carolina, including:

- ◆ 3 days deluxe accommodations
- ◆ air or travel credit
- ◆ 2 rounds of golf with cart
- ◆ daily golfer's breakfast

- ◆ reserved tee times ◆ awards banquets
- ◆ daily tournaments with other members
- ◆ hole-in-ones for $100,000!
- ◆ shoot-outs for $1,000,000!

Wild Dunes
Charleston's island resort

"....the trip, accommodations, food and golf were excellent."
— Mark Gilligan, 1997 Hole-In-One Winner

"...They stage a first class event for all their guests."
— Dave Selner, Golf Group Coordinator, Wild Dunes

GOLF MARKETING
I N C O R P O R A T E D

#1 Hole-in-One Insurance, Award, and Prize Package Company

MAIL IN OR CALL TODAY!
(800) 474-5556

Receive your certificate of membership to the HOLE-IN-ONE CLUB!
For only **$12.95** you can secure your chance to win the golf vacation of a lifetime. You could score your next ace tomorrow. So don't hesitate.
JOIN TODAY and MAKE A HOLE-IN-ONE in 1998

NAME _____

ADDRESS _____

STATE, CITY, ZIP _____

MAIL TO: Golf Marketing Inc., 109 Haverhill Street, N. Reading, MA 01864

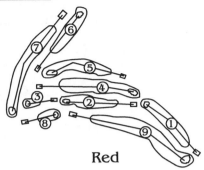

Red

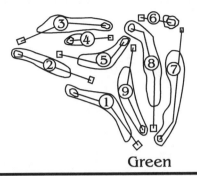

Green

SUNKEN MEADOW STATE PARK

Kings Park,NY   (PUBLIC)

Green\Red

GOLF COURSE 516 269-3838
TEE TIMES 516 269-0707

HOLES	YARDS blue\white\red	PAR	RATING blue\white\red	SLOPE blue\white\red
18	0000\6165\0000	72	00.0\00.0\00.0	000\116\000

HOLES	1	2	3	4	5	6	7	8	9	TOTAL
PAR	4	4	4	3	4	3	5	5	4	36
YARDS	350	385	395	175	340	145	470	485	380	3125
(Blue)	000	000	000	000	000	000	000	000	000	0000

HOLES	10	11	12	13	14	15	16	17	18	TOTAL
PAR	4	4	3	4	4	4	5	3	5	36
YARDS	305	300	130	410	375	345	505	155	515	3040
(Blue)	000	000	000	000	000	000	000	000	000	0000

GREEN FEES:$18 on weekdays,$22 weekends.**First Tee Off:**6am.**Tee Times:**Call 7 days
in advance with a photo ID card.Cards can be purchased at Sunken
Meadow,Montauk Downs or Bethpage.The card cost is $25 and is valid for
3 years.There is a $3 reservation fee per golfer.

ARCHITECT: Alfred Tull
YEAR BUILT:1953
PRO: Kevin Smith,PGA
SEASON: April-December

DISCOUNTS: Seniors
CART FEES:$14 for 9,$24 for 18.
SPIKE POLICY: Soft spikes preferred
AVAILABLE FOR TOURNAMENTS:yes
CONTACT: Doug Molauder 516 269-4333
DAYS: Mon,Weds,Fri,only.Min 40,max 120.Start
after 11am,no shotgun starts.

COURSE DESCRIPTION: In 1998 there will be one 18 hole course and one 9 hole course.
The combination will rotate.The green course is the easiest to score on,but the longest.
The red course is very hilly.

FEATURES\FACILITIES:

DRIVING RANGE-yes
RESTAURANT-yes
LOUNGE-yes
LESSONS-yes
PRO SHOP-yes

BANQUET-yes
WOMEN'S LOCKERS-no
MEN'S LOCKERS-no
MEETING ROOM-yes
NEARBY LODGING-yes

PRACTICE AREA-yes
BAR-yes
RENTAL CLUBS-yes
CREDIT CARDS-no
SNACK BAR-yes

DIRECTIONS:495 LIE to exit 53N (Sunken Meadow Parkway).Proceed North to the Park
and the course.

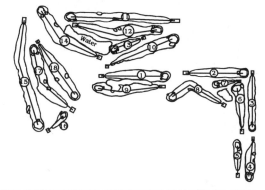

SWAN LAKE GC (SEMI-PRIVATE)

Manorville,NY

Course

GOLF COURSE 516 369-1818
TEE TIMES 516 369-1818

HOLES	YARDS blue\white\red	PAR	RATING blue\white\red	SLOPE blue\white\red
18	7011\6338\5245	72	72.5\69.5\69.0	121\115\112

HOLES	1	2	3	4	5	6	7	8	9	TOTAL
PAR	4	4	5	4	3	5	3	4	4	36
YARDS	357	370	481	307	177	467	153	354	343	3009
(Blue)	407	417	521	337	247	507	188	394	373	3391

HOLES	10	11	12	13	14	15	16	17	18	TOTAL
PAR	4	5	4	3	4	5	3	4	4	36
YARDS	383	547	431	177	373	507	124	393	394	3329
(Blue)	418	577	466	222	393	537	150	433	424	3620

GREEN FEES:$27 on weekdays,$30 weekends.**First Tee Off:**6am.**Tee Times:**Call 7 days in advance.There is a $25 charge per party.Course sells seasonal reserved Tee Times for weekends only.Call for details.

ARCHITECT:N\A
YEAR BUILT:1979
PRO: Sam Panasci,PGA
SEASON: All year

DISCOUNTS: Twilight (after 3pm) 2 golfers and cart $56 weekdays,$62 weekends.
CART FEES:$26
SPIKE POLICY: Soft spikes required
AVAILABLE FOR TOURNAMENTS:yes
CONTACT: Sam Panasci **DAYS:**Mon-Fri min 40-max 160.

COURSE DESCRIPTION: This is a well maintained,picturesque course with water on half of the holes.The fairways are wide and the greens are large.

FEATURES\FACILITIES:

DRIVING RANGE-no
RESTAURANT-yes
LOUNGE-yes
LESSONS-no
PRO SHOP-yes

BANQUET-yes
WOMEN'S LOCKERS-no
MEN'S LOCKERS-yes
MEETING ROOM-no
NEARBY LODGING-no

PRACTICE AREA-yes
BAR-yes
RENTAL CLUBS-yes
CREDIT CARDS-yes
SNACK BAR-yes

DIRECTIONS: 495 LIE to exit 70.Make a left and proceed to end of road.Make a right onto Ryerson St.At stop sign make a right onto North St.Bear left at the fork and go ½ mile to River Rd and make a right.Proceed to course on the left.

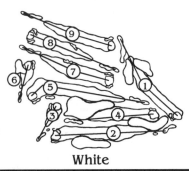

White

Blue

TIMBER POINT GC (PUBLIC)

Great River,NY

White\Blue

GOLF COURSE 516 581-2401

TEE TIMES 516 244-7275

HOLES	YARDS blue\white\red	PAR	RATING blue\white\red	SLOPE blue\white\red
18	6642\5993\5367	72	72.9\70.8\72.5	121\117\119

HOLES	1	2	3	4	5	6	7	8	9	TOTAL
PAR	4	5	3	4	5	3	4	4	4	36
YARDS	302	455	133	343	467	118	370	352	385	2925
(Blue)	344	488	158	369	489	138	397	376	403	3162

HOLES	10	11	12	13	14	15	16	17	18	TOTAL
PAR	5	3	4	4	3	4	4	5	4	36
YARDS	458	133	368	417	188	343	388	468	405	3168
(Blue)	488	146	381	435	208	366	422	490	427	3363

GREEN FEES:$19 on weekdays,$20 weekends.**First Tee Off:**7am.**Tee Times:**You must
(Residents)   be a Suffolk County resident with a Green Key Card.Card holders can
call 7 days in advance,or day before from a touch tone phone.There is a
$3 reservation fee per golfer.

GREEN FEES:$28 on weekdays,$32 on weekends.**Tee Times:**Non-residents can not call
(Non-resident)   for reservations.They must walk on.

ARCHITECT:N\A
YEAR BUILT:1927
PRO: Andrew Carracino,PGA
SEASON: Mar 13-Jan 25

DISCOUNTS: Seniors and Twilight
CART FEES:$25 for 18,$16 for 9.
SPIKE POLICY: Soft spikes required
AVAILABLE FOR TOURNAMENTS:yes
CONTACT: Andrew Carracino **DAYS:**Call for details.

COURSE DESCRIPTION: These three 9 hole courses are links style.The great South Bay
borders a few holes.

FEATURES\FACILITIES:
DRIVING RANGE-yes
RESTAURANT-yes
LOUNGE-yes
LESSONS-yes
PRO SHOP-yes

BANQUET-yes
WOMEN'S LOCKERS-yes
MEN'S LOCKERS-yes
MEETING ROOM-no
NEARBY LODGING-no

PRACTICE AREA-yes
BAR-yes
RENTAL CLUBS-yes
CREDIT CARDS-yes
SNACK BAR-yes

DIRECTIONS: Southern State Parkway to exit 45 East (Montauk Highway).Make a right
at the first traffic light (Great River Rd).Proceed 1 ½ miles to course entrance.

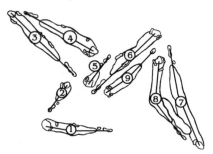
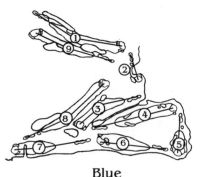

Red   Blue

TIMBER POINT GC   (PUBLIC)

Great River,NY
Red\Blue

GOLF COURSE 516 581-2401
TEE TIMES 516 244-7275

HOLES	YARDS blue\white\red	PAR	RATING blue\white\red	SLOPE blue\white\red
18	6525\6187\5455	72	71.9\69.9\71.5	116\111\115

HOLES	1	2	3	4	5	6	7	8	9	TOTAL
PAR	4	3	5	4	3	4	5	4	4	36
YARDS	298	147	450	425	172	358	482	400	287	3019
(Blue)	313	172	491	455	194	388	528	424	314	3279

HOLES	10	11	12	13	14	15	16	17	18	TOTAL
PAR	5	3	4	4	3	4	4	5	4	36
YARDS	458	133	368	417	188	343	388	468	405	3168
(Blue)	488	146	381	435	208	366	422	490	427	3363

GREEN FEES:$19 on weekdays,$20 weekends.**First Tee Off:**7am.**Tee Times:**You must
(Residents)   be a Suffolk County resident with a Green Key Card.Card holders can
call 7 days in advance,or day before from a touch tone phone.There is a
$3 reservation fee per golfer.

GREEN FEES:$28 on weekdays,$32 on weekends.**Tee Times:**Non-residents can not call
(Non-resident)   for reservations.They must walk on.

ARCHITECT:N\A
YEAR BUILT:1927
PRO: Andrew Carracino,PGA
SEASON: Mar 13-Jan 25

DISCOUNTS: Seniors and Twilight
CART FEES:$25 for 18,$16 for 9.
SPIKE POLICY: Soft spikes required
AVAILABLE FOR TOURNAMENTS:yes
CONTACT: Andrew Carracino **DAYS:**Call for details.

COURSE DESCRIPTION: These three 9 hole courses are links style.The great South Bay
borders a few holes.

FEATURES\FACILITIES:
DRIVING RANGE-yes
RESTAURANT-yes
LOUNGE-yes
LESSONS-yes
PRO SHOP-yes

BANQUET-yes
WOMEN'S LOCKERS-yes
MEN'S LOCKERS-yes
MEETING ROOM-no
NEARBY LODGING-no

PRACTICE AREA-yes
BAR-yes
RENTAL CLUBS-yes
CREDIT CARDS-yes
SNACK BAR-yes

DIRECTIONS: Southern State Parkway to exit 45 East (Montauk Highway).Make a right
at the first traffic light (Great River Rd).Proceed 1 ½ miles to course entrance.

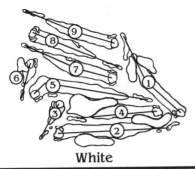

White

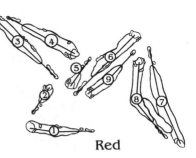

Red

TIMBER POINT GC (PUBLIC)

Great River,NY

White\Red

GOLF COURSE 516 581-2401
TEE TIMES 516 244-7275

HOLES	YARDS blue\white\red	PAR	RATING blue\white\red	SLOPE blue\white\red
18	6441\5844\5358	72	70.6\68.4\70.5	116\111\114

HOLES	1	2	3	4	5	6	7	8	9	TOTAL
PAR	4	5	3	4	5	3	4	4	4	36
YARDS	302	455	133	343	467	118	370	352	385	2925
(Blue)	344	488	158	369	489	138	397	376	403	3162

HOLES	10	11	12	13	14	15	16	17	18	TOTAL
PAR	4	3	5	4	3	4	5	4	4	36
YARDS	298	147	450	425	172	358	482	400	287	3019
(Blue)	313	172	491	455	194	388	528	424	314	3279

GREEN FEES:$19 on weekdays,$20 weekends.**First Tee Off:**7am.**Tee Times:**You must
(Residents) be a Suffolk County resident with a Green Key Card.Card holders can
call 7 days in advance,or day before from a touch tone phone.There is a
$3 reservation fee per golfer.

GREEN FEES:$28 on weekdays,$32 on weekends.**Tee Times:**Non-residents can not call
(Non-resident) for reservations.They must walk on.

ARCHITECT:N\A
YEAR BUILT:1927
PRO: Andrew Carracino,PGA
SEASON: Mar 13-Jan 25

DISCOUNTS: Seniors and Twilight
CART FEES:$25 for 18,$16 for 9.
SPIKE POLICY: Soft spikes required
AVAILABLE FOR TOURNAMENTS:yes
CONTACT: Andrew Carracino **DAYS:**Call for details.

COURSE DESCRIPTION: These three 9 hole courses are links style.The great South Bay
borders a few holes.

FEATURES\FACILITIES:

DRIVING RANGE-yes
RESTAURANT-yes
LOUNGE-yes
LESSONS-yes
PRO SHOP-yes

BANQUET-yes
WOMEN'S LOCKERS-yes
MEN'S LOCKERS-yes
MEETING ROOM-no
NEARBY LODGING-no

PRACTICE AREA-yes
BAR-yes
RENTAL CLUBS-yes
CREDIT CARDS-yes
SNACK BAR-yes

DIRECTIONS: Southern State Parkway to exit 45 East (Montauk Highway).Make a right
at the first traffic light (Great River Rd).Proceed 1 ½ miles to course entrance.

WEST SAYVILLE GC (PUBLIC)
West Sayville,NY
Course

GOLF COURSE 516 567-1704
TEE TIMES 516 244-PARK

HOLES	YARDS blue\white\red	PAR	RATING blue\white\red	SLOPE blue\white\red
18	6715\6130\5387	72	72.1\69.5\70.1	127\122\120

HOLES	1	2	3	4	5	6	7	8	9	TOTAL
PAR	5	3	4	4	5	4	4	3	4	36
YARDS	485	143	317	372	475	367	370	165	398	3092
(Blue)	515	178	365	402	505	405	395	195	426	3386

HOLES	10	11	12	13	14	15	16	17	18	TOTAL
PAR	4	5	3	4	5	4	4	3	4	36
YARDS	355	472	170	372	473	363	367	123	343	3038
(Blue)	385	502	195	401	500	403	392	175	376	3329

GREEN FEES:$19 on weekdays,$20 weekends.**First Tee Off:**6am.**Tee Times:**You must
(Resident)   be a Suffolk County resident with a Green Key Card.Card holders can call
7 days in advance or day before from a touch tone phone.There is a
$3 reservation fee per golfer.

GREEN FEES:$28 on weekdays,$32 on weekends.**Tee Times:**Non-residents can not call
(Non-resident)   for reservations.They must walk on.

ARCHITECT: William Mitchell
YEAR BUILT:1967
PRO: Fred Gipp,PGA
SEASON: March-January

DISCOUNTS: Seniors and Twilight
CART FEES:$26
SPIKE POLICY: Soft spikes required
AVAILABLE FOR TOURNAMENTS:yes
CONTACT: Fred Gipp **DAYS:**Monday
start after 11:30am.

COURSE DESCRIPTION: This is a links style course,well bunkered and some water.Fair
test from the blue markers.

FEATURES\FACILITIES:
DRIVING RANGE-yes
RESTAURANT-yes
LOUNGE-yes
LESSONS-yes
PRO SHOP-yes

BANQUET-yes
WOMEN'S LOCKERS-no
MEN'S LOCKERS-no
MEETING ROOM-no
NEARBY LODGING-no

PRACTICE AREA-yes
BAR-yes
RENTAL CLUBS-yes
CREDIT CARDS-yes
SNACK BAR-yes

DIRECTIONS:495 LIE to exit 57 (Veterans Memorial Hwy.).Proceed 4 ½ miles to Lakeland
Ave and make a right.Proceed to the end of road (Montauk Hwy) and make a right.Proceed
1 mile to course on the left.

PRIVATE COURSES

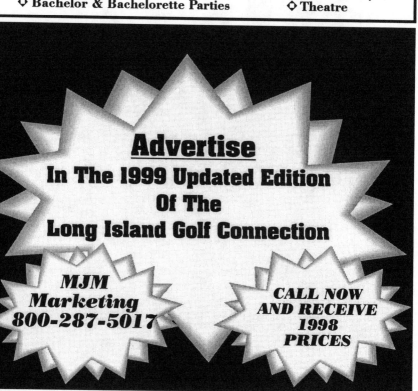

PRIVATE COURSES

ATLANTIC GOLF CLUB
Bridgehampton, NY

GOLF COURSE 516 537-1818
PRO: Rick Hartmann,PGA

DIRECTIONS:495 LIE to exit 70. Make a right at the stop sign and proceed to the end. Turn left onto Route 27 East. Follow 27 for 20 miles to T-intersection. Make a left the T-intersection on Scuttle Hole Rd. Make the first left after the HESS station and proceed 2 miles to the course.

BELLPORT CC
Bellport, NY

GOLF COURSE 516 286-7206
PRO: Leo McMahon,PGA

DIRECTIONS:495 LIE to exit 64 South. Proceed South on Route 112 to the end. Make a left onto Main St (Patchogue/Montauk Hwy). Proceed 1 ½ miles to the fork and bear right on South County Rd. Club is 3 miles on the right.

BLUE RIDGE GC
Medford, NY

GOLF COURSE 516 698-8394
PRO: Currently None

DIRECTIONS:495 LIE to exit 64. Follow 112 North to Granny Rd. Make a left on Granny Rd. Follow to Blue Ridge Dr and make a left. Follow signs to the course.

BRETTON WOODS CC
Coram, NY

GOLF COURSE 516 698-4861
PRO: Currently None

DIRECTIONS:495 LIE to exit 63. Proceed North on Country Road 83 for 5 miles and make a right onto Mooney Park Rd. Proceed 1 mile to the course on the right.

BRIDGEHAMPTON CLUB
Bridgehampton, NY

GOLF COURSE 516 537-9875
PRO: CurrentlyNone

DIRECTIONS:495 LIE to exit 70. Make a right and proceed to the end. Turn left onto Route 27 East. Proceed to Bridgehampton and make a right onto Ocean Rd (near war monument). Club is ½ mile on the left.

BROOKVILLE CC
Glen Head, NY

GOLF COURSE 516 671-8466
PRO: Doug Miller,PGA

DIRECTIONS:495 LIE to exit 41 (Route 107 North). Proceed to Hageman's Lane and make a right (first right after 25A). Proceed to the end and follow signs for the course.

CEDAR BROOK G&TC
Old Brookville, NY

GOLF COURSE 516 759-8447
PRO: June Staton,PGA

DIRECTIONS:495 LIE to exit 41 (Route 107 North). Proceed to Chicken Valley Rd and make a right. Proceed 1 mile to Oak Lane. Club entrance is on the left.

CHERRY VALLEY CLUB
Garden City, NY

GOLF COURSE 516 741-1980
PRO: Ed Kelly,PGA

DIRECTIONS:495 LIE to exit 34 South. Take New Hyde Park Rd to Stewart Ave, and make a left. Proceed 2 miles to Cherry Valley Ave and make a right. Club is ½ mile on the right.

PRIVATE COURSES

COLD SPRING CC
Cold Spring Harbor, NY

GOLF COURSE 516 367-3513
PRO:Tom Herzog,PGA

DIRECTIONS:495 LIE to exit 44N (Seaford Oyster Bay Expressway) Route 135. Take 135 to the exit for Route 25 (Jericho Tpke) East. Proceed 3 miles to club entrance on the left.

CREEK CLUB
Locust Valley, NY

GOLF COURSE 516 671-1001
PRO:John Sanges,PGA

DIRECTIONS:495 LIE to exit 39N (Glen Cove Rd). Proceed North for 5 miles, at fork turn left onto Route 107 North. Proceed to the end and make a right on Brewster St. Brewster will become Forest Ave. Proceed 1 ½ miles to Lattingtown Rd and bear left. First light turn left to club entrance.

DEEPDALE GC
Manhasset, NY

GOLF COURSE 516 627-7880
PRO:Darrell Kestner,PGA

DIRECTIONS:495 LIE to exit 34. Cross over the expressway and make a left onto the service road going West. Club entrance is on the right.

ENGINEERS CC
Roslyn Harbor, NY

GOLF COURSE 516 621-5350
PRO:Eric Feltman,PGA

DIRECTIONS:495 LIE to exit 37 Willis Ave. Make a left on Willis and proceed to 25A and make a right. Proceed to first right-hand exit after the bridge. Bear right at the light and make a right on Bryant Ave. Proceed to Glenwood Rd. Entrance is ½ mile on the right.

FISHERS ISLAND CC
Fishers Island, NY

GOLF COURSE 516 788-7221
PRO:Tom O'Brien,PGA

DIRECTIONS: Call for directions.

FRESH MEADOW CC
Great Neck,NY

GOLF COURSE 516 482-7300
PRO:Charlie Bolling,PGA

DIRECTIONS:495 LIE to exit 33. Make a left onto Lakeville Rd.and proceed ½ mile to Club entrance on the right.

GARDEN CITY CC
Garden City, NY

GOLF COURSE 516 747-2929
PRO:Don Beatty,PGA

DIRECTIONS:495 LIE to exit 34. Proceed South on New Hyde Park Rd., To Stewart Ave and make a left. Proceed 1 mile to the club entrance on the right.

GARDEN CITY GC
Garden City, NY

GOLF COURSE 516 746-8360
PRO:Gil McNally,PGA

DIRECTIONS:495 LIE to exit 34. Proceed South on New Hyde Park Rd., To Stewart Ave and make a left. Proceed 2 miles and turn left on Cherry Valley Rd. Entrance to the club is on the left.

PRIVATE COURSES

GARDINEERS BAY CC
Shelter Island, NY

GOLF COURSE 516 749-0625
PRO:Bob DeStefano,PGA

DIRECTIONS:495 LIE to exit 70. Take Route 111 to Sunrise Hwy (Route 27) East. Follow Sunrise into Southampton. When the road merges with Montauk Hwy, continue on into Bridge Hampton. Make a left on Bridge Hampton/Sag Harbor Rd (Route 79). Follow this all the way till the road merges with Route 114. Go North on 114 and follow signs for the ferry. When on Shelter Island, proceed to Winthrop Ave and cross over Gardineers Creek. At the fork bear right onto Cobbetts Lane. At 1st intersection, make left on Manhasset Rd to club.

GLEN HEAD CC
Glen Head, NY

GOLF COURSE 516 676-4057
PRO:Scott Hawkins,PGA

DIRECTIONS:495 LIE to exit 39 North. Proceed on Glen Cove Rd until it joins Route 107 (Cedar Swamp Rd). Look for club signs and entrance on the left.

GLEN OAKS CC
Old Westbury, NY

GOLF COURSE 516 626-0161
PRO:Tom Joyce,PGA

DIRECTIONS:495 LIE to exit 39 South. Stay on the service road to Post Rd and make a left. Proceed ½ mile to club entrance on the right.

THE HAMLETS CC
Commack, NY

GOLF COURSE 516 499-5200
PRO:Jim Thompson,PGA

DIRECTIONS:495 LIE to exit 52 North (Commack Rd). Go 5 traffic lights on Commack Rd and make a left on Hauppauge Rd. The club is 400 Yds on the left.

HAMPTON HILLS G&CC
West Hampton Beach, NY

GOLF COURSE 516 727-6862
PRO:Jack McGowan,PGA

DIRECTIONS:495 LIE to exit 70. Make a right and proceed to the end. Make a left onto 27 East to Exit 63 North. Proceed ½ mile to club entrance on the left.

HAY HARBOR GC
Fishers Island, NY

GOLF COURSE 516 788-7514
PRO:Gene Mulak,PGA

DIRECTIONS:Call for directions.

HEMPSTEAD G&CC
Hempstead, NY

GOLF COURSE 516 481-7411
PRO:Walter Ostroske,PGA

DIRECTIONS: Southern State Parkway to Exit 39 North (Peninsula Blvd). Proceed to Presidents St and make a left at the third traffic light onto Front St. At the first light make a left to the club entrance.

HUNTINGTON CC
Huntington, NY

GOLF COURSE 516 427-0876
PRO:Jim Smoot,PGA

DIRECTIONS:495 LIE to exit 41 North. Proceed on Route 106/107 North to fork. Bear right on Route 106 and proceed 3 ½ miles to Route 25A. Make right on 25A and head East through Cold Spring Harbor to the club entrance on the left.

PRIVATE COURSES

HUNTINGTON CRESCENT CLUB **GOLF COURSE 516 421-5180**
Huntington, NY **PRO:**John Schob,PGA

DIRECTIONS:495 LIE to exit 49 North. Go North on Route 110 to Route 25A (Main St) and make a right. Proceed on 25A to Washington Dr and bear left. Proceed to Club entrance on the left.

INDIAN HILLS CC **GOLF COURSE 516 757-7718**
Northport, NY **PRO:**Joe Laurentino,PGA

DIRECTIONS:495 LIE to exit 53 North (Sunken Meadow State Pkwy). Proceed to Route 25A West, go 2 ½ miles to Fresh Pond Rd and make a right. Go 2 blocks to Breeze Hill Rd and make a left. Proceed to top of the hill. Club entrance is on the left.

INWOOD CC **GOLF COURSE 516 239-4454**
Inwood, NY **PRO:**Tommy Thomas,PGA

DIRECTIONS: Southern State Parkway to Exit 19S (Peninsula Blvd). Proceed South and cross over Rockaway Turnpike. At the light make a left and follow the signs to Burnside Ave. Burnside becomes Sheridan Ave. Proceed to turn and stay straight onto Bayswater Blvd. Proceed to Peppe Dr and make a right to club.

ISLAND HILLS GC **GOLF COURSE 516 563-1492**
Sayville, NY **PRO:**Harvey Lannak,PGA

DIRECTIONS:495 LIE to exit 57. Make a right onto Veterans Memorial Hwy (Route 454). Proceed to Lakeland Ave and make right. Cross Route 27 to Club.

LAKE SUCCESS GC **GOLF COURSE 516 482-4012**
Lake Success, NY **PRO:**Robert Mistretta,PGA

DIRECTIONS:495 LIE to exit 33. Proceed South on Lakeville Rd for ½ mile to the club.

LAWRENCE GC **GOLF COURSE 516 239-8263**
Lawrence, NY **PRO:**Craig Thomas,PGA

DIRECTIONS: Southern State Pkwy to Exit 19 South. Proceed South for 7 miles to Rockaway Blvd and make a left. The road changes to Meadow Lane, Continue for 1 ½ miles to causeway and make a left. Club entrance is on the right.

MAIDSTONE CLUB **GOLF COURSE 516 324-0510**
East Hampton, NY **PRO:**Eden Foster,PGA

DIRECTIONS:495 LIE to exit 70. Make a right and proceed to the end. Make a left onto Route 27 and proceed East to East Hampton. Make a left at the T-intersection on Route 27 and continue to the end of the village green (flag pole & summer theatre are landmarks). Make a right and proceed ½ mile to the club.

MEADOWBROOK CC **GOLF COURSE 516 822-3354**
Jericho, NY **PRO:**Rick Meskell,PGA

DIRECTIONS:495 LIE to exit 41 North. Proceed North on Route 106/107, bear left onto Route 107. Proceed ½ mile to where the road narrows and make a U-turn. Club entrance is immediately on the right.

PRIVATE COURSES

MIDDLE BAY CC **GOLF COURSE 516 766-1880**
Oceanside, NY **PRO:**Tim Shifflett,PGA

DIRECTIONS: Southern State Pkw to Exit 20 South. Proceed on Grand Ave for 3 ½ miles to Atlantic Ave and make a right. Proceed ½ mile to Waukena Ave and make a left. Proceed ½ mile to Skillman Ave and make a left. Club is on the left.

MILL RIVER CLUB **GOLF COURSE 516 922-3556**
Upper Brookville, NY **PRO:**Mark Mielke,PGA

DIRECTIONS:495 LIE to exit 41 North. Proceed North on 106 to Northern Blvd (Route 25A) and make a left. Proceed to Mill River Rd and make a right. Club is 1 mile on the left.

MUTTONTOWN GOLF & CC **GOLF COURSE 516 922-3324**
E. Norwich, NY **PRO:**Roger Ginsberg,PGA

DIRECTIONS:495 LIE to exit 41 North. Proceed North on Route 106 to Northern Blvd (Route 25A) and make a left. Proceed 1 mile to the club entrance on the right.

NASSAU CC **GOLF COURSE 516 759-3020**
Glen Cove, NY **PRO:**Harold Kolb,PGA

DIRECTIONS:495 LIE to exit 39 North. Proceed North on Glen Cove Rd for 5 miles to fork and bear right. Cross over RR tracks to Pearsall Ave and make a right. Proceed ½ mile to club entrance on the right.

NATIONAL GOLF LINKS **GOLF COURSE 516 283-0410**
Southampton, NY **PRO:**Michael Muller,PGA

DIRECTIONS:495 LIE to exit 70. Turn right and proceed South to the end. Make a left onto 27 East. When the road narrows to two lanes, proceed 1 mile to Sebonac Rd. Proceed past Cold Spring Harbor Rd, then make a hard left, continuing on Sebonac Rd to the end. Follow signs to the club.

NISSEQUOGUE GC **GOLF COURSE 516 584-2453**
St James, NY **PRO:**John Elwood,PGA

DIRECTIONS:495 LIE to exit 53 North (Sunken Meadow Pkwy) to Route 25 East (Jericho Tpke). Proceed 4 ½ miles and turn left onto Edgewood Ave. Proceed 1 mile to Nissquogue/River Rd and make a left. Proceed ½ mile to club entrance on the right.

NORTH FORK CC **GOLF COURSE 516 734-7758**
Cutchogue, NY **PRO:**Peter Cowan,PGA

DIRECTIONS:495 LIE to exit 73. Proceed East 3 miles to Route 58. Continue on 58 till the road merges with Route 25. Continue on 25 for 10 miles to Cutchogue. Club entrance is on the right.

NORTH HEMPSTEAD CC **GOLF COURSE 516 365-7500**
Port Washington, NY **PRO:**Greg Hurd,PGA

DIRECTIONS:495 LIE to exit 36. Proceed North on Searingtown Road, Crossing Northern Blvd. Road changes to Port Washington Blvd. Proceed North 1 ½ miles to the club entrance on the right.

PRIVATE COURSES

NORTH HILLS CC
Manhassett, NY

GOLF COURSE 516 627-9139
PRO: Mike Caporale,PGA

DIRECTIONS:495 LIE to exit 35 Shelter Rock Rd. At thr first traffic light make a left crossing the expressway. At the next traffic light make a left onto the Westbound Service Rd to the club entrance on the right.

NORTH SHORE CC
Glen Head, NY

GOLF COURSE 516 676-4225
PRO: Bill Burke,PGA

DIRECTIONS:495 LIE to exit 39N. Proceed North on Glen Cove Rd to Glen Head Rd and make a left. Glen Head Rd becomes Glenwood Rd. Proceed to the end and make a right on Shore Rd and follow signs to the club.

NOYAC GOLF & CC
Sag Harbor, NY

GOLF COURSE 516 725-1889
PRO: Dave Gosiewski,PGA

DIRECTIONS:495 LIE to exit 70. Turn right and take to the end. Make a left on Route 27 East and proceed for approximately 16 ½ miles to exit 8. Bear left toward Noyac/North Sea/Shelter Island. Proceed to North Sea Rd and make a left. Proceed to the fork and bear right onto Noyac Rd. Take Noyac Rd for 5 miles to Wildwood Rd and make a right. Club entrance is on the right.

OLD WESTBURY GOLF & CC
Old Westbury, NY

GOLF COURSE 516 626-1220
PRO: Jim Andrews,PGA

DIRECTIONS:495 LIE to exit 39 South. Continue East on Service road for 8/10 of mile to Wheatley Rd and make second left onto Wheatley. Go for 1 ¼ miles to dead end. Make a left and go 5/10 mile to club entrance.

PINE HOLLOW CC
East Norwich, NY

GOLF COURSE 516 922-0300
PRO: Tom DeBellis,PGA

DIRECTIONS:495 LIE to exit 41 North. Proceed on Route 106 North to Route 25A (Northern Blvd) and make a right. Go 7/10 mile to course.

PIPING ROCK CLUB
Locust Valley, NY

GOLF COURSE 516 676-0460
PRO: Iain Mossman,PGA

DIRECTIONS:495 LIE to exit 39N (Glen Cove Rd). Make a right on Route 25A, following down past colleges and police station. Make a left on Wover Rd. Go 2 miles and make a left on Piping Rock Rd. Follow signs to course.

PLANDOME CC
Plandome, NY

GOLF COURSE 516 627-1273
PRO: Jim Hundertmark,PGA

DIRECTIONS:495 LIE to exit 36 North. Follow till you pass Northern Blvd, continue 4-5 lights past Northern Blvd and make a left on Stoneytown Rd. Go under the RR tressle and the club is on the right side.

PORT JEFFERSON CC
Port Jefferson, NY

GOLF COURSE 516 473-1440
PRO: John Kim,PGA

DIRECTIONS:495 LIE to exit 64 (Route 112). Go North to the end. Make a right on East Broadway, follow to stop sign and thn go straight past stop sign. Make first left on Oakwood Rd and then make a left on Winston Dr. Follow to course.

PRIVATE COURSES

QUOGUE FIELD CLUB   **GOLF COURSE 516 653-9885**
Quogue, NY   **PRO:**Rich Stucklen,PGA

DIRECTIONS: Call for directions.

ROCKAWAY HUNTING CLUB   **GOLF COURSE 516 569-0600**
Lawrence, NY   **PRO:**Randy Cavanaugh,PGA

DIRECTIONS: Belt Parkway to Rockaway Blvd East. Follow down Rockaway and make a left on Broadway. Go ¼ mile and make a right on Cedarhurst Ave. Go ½ mile and make a left on Ocean Avenue. Follow signs to the course.

ROCKVILLE LINKS CC   **GOLF COURSE 516 766-7446**
Rockville Centre, NY   **PRO:**Mike Turnesa Jr.,PGA

DIRECTIONS: Southern State Pkwy to Exit 19S (Peninsula Blvd). Go across Peninsula as if entering the hospital. Make right on Village Ave. Go to 1st traffic light and make aleft on Demott. Make a left on Long Beach Rd and the club is on the left side.

SANDS POINT GC   **GOLF COURSE 516 883-3130**
Sands Point, NY   **PRO:**Rick Haldas,PGA

DIRECTIONS:495 LIE to exit 36. Make a left at the light at Searingtown Rd. Go 7-8 miles and the road changes to Port Washington Blvd, then Middle Neck Rd. Club is on the left.

SEAWANE CLUB   **GOLF COURSE 516 374-1110**
Hewlett Harbor, NY   **PRO:**Bob Longo,PGA

DIRECTIONS: Southern State Pkwy to Exit 13 (Central Ave/Valley Stream). Central Ave changes to Mill Rd after crossing Sunrise Hwy. Take Mill to the end and make a left on W. Broadway. Go 2 traffic lights and make a right on East Rockaway Rd. Go ¼ mile and make a right on Schenck Rd. Go to the end and make a right on Club Dr.

SHINNECOCK HILLS GC   **GOLF COURSE 516 283-1310**
Southampton, NY   **PRO:**Don McDougall,PGA

DIRECTIONS:495 LIE to exit 70. Make a right and proceed South on Route 111 to Sunrise Hwy. Proceed East on Sunrise Hwy until it turns into North County Rd 39. Proceed to Southampton and follow North County Rd to Tuckahoe Rd and make aleft to the course.

SOUTH FORK CC   **GOLF COURSE 516 267-6827**
Amagansett, NY   **PRO:**John Eisen,PGA

DIRECTIONS:495 LIE to exit 70. Proceed South on Route 111 to 27 East Proceed into the town of Amagansett. Proceed through town at fork go over RR tracks. The course is 100 yards on the left.

SOUTHAMPTON GOLF CLUB   **GOLF COURSE 516 283-9850**
Southampton, NY   **PRO:**Tim Garvin,PGA

DIRECTIONS:495 LIE to exit 70. Take Sunrise Hwy East past Shinnecock Golf Club (going 10 miles). Club on the left side across from the Southampton driving range, just before the Elks club.

PRIVATE COURSES

SOUTHWARD HO
Bayshore, NY

GOLF COURSE 516 665-1753
PRO: Mike Darrell,PGA

DIRECTIONS: Southern State Pkwy to Exit 40 South. Take the Robert Moses Causeway to the second exit (RM2 East). Follow Montauk Hwy for 1 mile and course is on the left.

ST. GEORGE'S G & CC
Stony Brook, NY

GOLF COURSE 516 751-0585
PRO: Rod Heller,PGA

DIRECTIONS:495 LIE to exit 62 North. Follow for 6 miles and make a right on Sheep Pasture Rd. Follow winding road to the course.

TAM O'SHANTER GOLF CLUB
Brookville, NY

GOLF COURSE 516 626-1980
PRO: Mark Brown,PGA

DIRECTIONS:495 LIE to exit 41 North. Proceed North at the fork stay left onto Route 107. Proceed approx. 1 ½ miles to Fruitledge Rd and make a right. Proceed ½ mile to course on the right.

TOWERS CC
Lake Success, NY

GOLF COURSE 718 279-1848
PRO: Robert Guido,PGA

DIRECTIONS: Grand Central Pkwy to Exit 23 (Little Neck Parkway). Go straight on the service road to the Towers. Make a right into the Towers and follow signs for the course.

VILLAGE OF SANDS POINT
Sands Point, NY

GOLF COURSE 516 944-7840
PRO: Pam Cunningham,PGA

DIRECTIONS:495 LIE to exit 36. Make a left under the overpass, heading North. Go 5 miles to course on the right.

WESTHAMPTON CC
Westhampton, NY

GOLF COURSE 516 288-1110
PRO: Bobby Jenkins,PGA

DIRECTIONS:495 LIE to exit 70 (Route 111) South. Take 111 to Sunrise Hwy (Route 27) East. Take this to exit 63 (Old Riverhead Rd). Go 4 ½ miles South on Old Riverhead Rd and make a right on South Rd. Follow to the course.

WHEATLEY HILLS GC
East Williston, NY

GOLF COURSE 516 747-7358
PRO: Mike Gilmore,PGA

DIRECTIONS:495 LIE to exit 39S. (Glen Cove Rd). Make a right on Glen Cove Rd and follow to Hillside Ave. Turn right on Hillside Ave and follow signs to the course.

WOODCREST CLUB
Syosset, NY

GOLF COURSE 516 921-7800
PRO: Jon Kudysch,PGA

DIRECTIONS:495 LIE to exit 41 North. Take 106/107 North to Route 106. Take 106 to second traffic light and make a right on Eastwood Rd. Course is ½ mile on the right.

WOODMERE CC
Woodmere, NY

GOLF COURSE 516 295-2717
PRO: Joe Moresco,PGA

DIRECTIONS: Southern State Parkway to exit 19S. Proceed 6 miles to Woodmere Blvd and make a left. Proceed to Broadway and make a right. Proceed ½ mile to Meadow Dr and make a left to course.

DRIVING RANGES

CANTIAGUE PARK DRIVING DRANGE   Range 516 932-1600
Hicksville, NY

$4 Token 36 Balls
$10 Card 108 Balls
$25 Card 288 Balls
$50 Card 612 Balls
$100 Card 1296 Balls
PRO: Jeff Lollo

STATIONS:38-mats
LEVELS:1
COVERED:yes-19
HEATED:yes-19
LIGHTS:yes

HOURS: In season 7am - 11pm. Off season 8am - 8pm.

FEATURES\FACILITIES:

PRO SHOP:yes	PRACTICE AREA:yes	DISTANCE MARKERS:yes-flags
SNACK BAR:no	PUTTING GREEN:yes	LESSONS:yes
MINIATURE GOLF:yes	SAND TRAPS:yes	SEASONAL:no

DISCOUNTS: Breakfast special 7am-10am, Mon-Fri, 200 balls for $10.00.
DIRECTIONS:LIE (495) to Exit 41 South (Route 106/107). At fork in the road stay right. Make a right turn on W. John Street and follow down for 1-2 miles. Cantiague Park will be on the right. Turn into the park and the range is on the left.

DRIVING RANGE

COMMACK GOLF CENTER   Range 516 499-7007
Commack, NY

BUCKETS:
SMALL $4.00
MEDIUM $7.50
LARGE $12.50 -200 Balls
PRO: Fred Caruso,Don Jarvis
      Walter Sturge,Kate McKillop
HOURS: In season 7am-11pm.Off season 8am-8pm.

STATIONS:120
LEVELS:2
COVERED:yes-60
HEATED:yes
LIGHTS:yes

FEATURES\FACILITIES:

PRO SHOP:yes	PRACTICE AREA:yes	DISTANCE MARKERS:yes-flags
SNACK BAR:yes	PUTTING GREEN:yes	LESSONS:yes
MINIATURE GOLF:yes	SAND TRAPS:yes	SEASONAL:no

DISCOUNTS: Early bird special before 11am, includes jumbo bucket, coffee and bagel for $10.00.
DIRECTIONS:LIE (495) to Exit 52. Go to light and make a left on Commack Rd. Go ¼ mile and make right on Henry Street. Follow to the end and range is on the left.

DRIVING RANGE

FAMILY GOLF CENTERS AT ROCKY POINT   Range 516 821-7500
Rocky Point, NY   Pro Shop 516 821-7506

BUCKETS:
SMALL $4.00
MEDIUM $7.50
LARGE $10.00
PRO: Jim Haughy

STATIONS:70-mats
LEVELS:2
COVERED:yes-70
HEATED:yes-35
LIGHTS:yes

HOURS: In season 8am-9pm weekdays, 7am-10pm weekends. Off season varies 8am-8pm.

FEATURES\FACILITIES:

PRO SHOP:yes	PRACTICE AREA:yes	DISTANCE MARKERS:yes-flags
SNACK BAR:no	PUTTING GREEN:yes	LESSONS:yes
MINIATURE GOLF:no	SAND TRAPS:yes	SEASONAL:no

DISCOUNTS: Seniors $1.00 off a bucket. Everyday Special 10 pk. For $25.00

DIRECTIONS:LIE (495) to Exit 63. Take Route 83 North to Route 25A. Make a right on 25A and go 3 miles East to driving range on the left side.

DRIVING RANGE

GATEWAY GOLF	Range 718 253-6816
Brooklyn, NY	

BUCKETS:
SMALL $5.25-40 Balls
LARGE $7.00-70 Balls
PRO: Ed Kuna, PGA

STATIONS:75-mats
LEVELS:1
COVERED:yes-20
HEATED:no
LIGHTS:yes

HOURS: In season 7:30am-12am,Off season 9am-5:30pm

FEATURES\FACILITIES:

PRO SHOP:no   PRACTICE AREA:no   DISTANCE MARKERS:yes-flags
SNACK BAR:no   PUTTING GREEN:no   LESSONS:yes
MINIATURE GOLF:yes   SAND TRAPS:no   SEASONAL:no

DISCOUNTS: Call for details.

DIRECTIONS: Southern State Parkway to the Belt Parkway. Take the Belt Parkway to Exit 11 South. Stay on Flatbush Avenue and the driving range is on the right.

DRIVING RANGE

GOLDEN BEAR GOLF CTR AT ALLEY POND	Range 718 225-9187
Douglaston, NY	

BUCKETS:
SMALL $7.00
LARGE $10.00
PRO: Jason Kang

STATIONS:80-mats
LEVELS:1
COVERED:yes-80
HEATED:yes
LIGHTS:yes

HOURS: All year 7am-10pm.

FEATURES\FACILITIES:

PRO SHOP:yes   PRACTICE AREA:yes   DISTANCE MARKERS:yes-flags
SNACK BAR:yes   PUTTING GREEN:yes   LESSONS:yes
MINIATURE GOLF:yes   SAND TRAPS:yes   SEASONAL:no

DISCOUNTS: Early bird special 7am-9am 204 balls for $10.00.

DIRECTIONS: Cross Island Parkway to Exit 31 East (Northern Blvd). Range is ¼ mile on the left side.

DRIVING RANGE

GOLDEN BEAR GOLF CTR AT SKYDRIVE	Range 516 694-4666
Farmingdale, NY	

BUCKETS:
SMALL $4.50
MEDIUM $8.00
LARGE $10.00
PRO: Paul,Bill,Jay or Doug

STATIONS:80-mats
LEVELS:2
COVERED:yes-40
HEATED:yes-40
LIGHTS:yes

HOURS: Off season 6am-10pm,Fri& Sat 6am-11pm.In Season 6am-11pm,Fri& Sat 6am-12am.

FEATURES\FACILITIES:

PRO SHOP:yes   PRACTICE AREA:yes   DISTANCE MARKERS:yes-flags
SNACK BAR:yes   PUTTING GREEN:yes   LESSONS:yes
MINIATURE GOLF:yes   SAND TRAPS:yes   SEASONAL:no

DISCOUNTS: Breakfast special off season 6am-12pm,in season 6am-10am, weekdays you get 2 tokens,coffee and danish for $10.Weekends you get a jumbo bucket of 200 balls, coffee and danish for$10.00.

DIRECTIONS:LIE (495) to Exit 42 South. Go to second traffic light and make a right on 110 South. Follow 110 for 3-4 miles and the range is on the right.

DRIVING RANGE

GOLFPORT   **Range 718 472-4653**
Long Island City, NY

BUCKETS: **STATIONS:**10-mats
SMALL $5.00   **LEVELS:**1
LARGE $8.00   **COVERED:**yes-10
SUPER SIZE $15.00   **HEATED:**yes-10
PRO: Vincent Pauroso   **LIGHTS:**yes

HOURS: In season 9am-9pm (M-F),9am-8pm (Sat & Sun)

FEATURES\FACILITIES:

PRO SHOP:yes	PRACTICE AREA:yes	DISTANCE MARKERS:yes-flags
SNACK BAR:no	PUTTING GREEN:yes	LESSONS:yes
MINIATURE GOLF:no	SAND TRAPS:no	SEASONAL:no

DISCOUNTS: Early bird special and after work special.Call for details.

DIRECTIONS:LIE (495) West to Van Dam Street. At the bottom of the ramp continue thru the light to Borden Ave to parking lot on the East River.

DRIVING RANGE

HAUPPAUGE DRIVING RANGE   **Range 516 724-7500**
Hauppauge, NY   **Pro Shop 516 724-7500**

BUCKETS: **STATIONS:**50-mats
SMALL $3.00   **LEVELS:**1
PRO: Kevin Beatty   **COVERED:**no
                                    HEATED:no
                                    LIGHTS:yes

HOURS: In season 8am-5pm

FEATURES\FACILITIES:

PRO SHOP:yes	PRACTICE AREA:yes	DISTANCE MARKERS:yes-flags
SNACK BAR:yes	PUTTING GREEN:yes	LESSONS:yes
MINIATURE GOLF:no	SAND TRAPS:no	SEASONAL:no

DISCOUNTS: None

DIRECTIONS:LIE (495) to Exit 57 West. Take Veterans Hwy (Route 454) 3 miles West to Junction with 347. Range is on 347 in the Hauppauge Golf Course.

DRIVING RANGE

HEARTLAND GOLF PARK   **Range 516 667-7400**
Deer Park, NY   **Pro Shop 516 667-7400**

BUCKETS: Purchase cards for   **STATIONS:**91-mats
computerized tee area.   **LEVELS:**2
                                    COVERED:yes-44
                                    HEATED:yes-44
PRO: Pat Diesu & Frank Gallina   **LIGHTS:**yes

HOURS: Open 24 hours all season.Winter hours 7am-12am, 7 days.

FEATURES\FACILITIES:

PRO SHOP:yes	PRACTICE AREA:yes	DISTANCE MARKERS:yes-lazer
SNACK BAR:yes	PUTTING GREEN:yes	LESSONS:yes
MINIATURE GOLF:yes	SAND TRAPS:yes	SEASONAL:no

DISCOUNTS: Special for group functions on miniture golf.

DIRECTIONS:LIE (495) to Exit 53 South Sagtikos Pkwy. Take the Sagtikos to Exit S3, Pine Aire Drive. Make a left a go ¼ mile down to range on the right.

INDIAN HEAD GOLF PARK   Range 516 269-4100
Kings Park, NY

BUCKETS: **STATIONS:**47
SMALL $5.00-45 Balls   **LEVELS:**1
MEDIUM $8.00-75 Balls   **COVERED:**no
LARGE $10-125 Balls   **HEATED:**no
PRO: Vincent Cirino   **LIGHTS:**yes

HOURS: In season Mon-Fri 8am-11pm. Sat and Sun 7am-11pm.

FEATURES\FACILITIES:

PRO SHOP:yes   PRACTICE AREA:yes   DISTANCE MARKERS:yes-greens
SNACK BAR:no   PUTTING GREEN:no   LESSONS:yes
MINIATURE GOLF:no   SAND TRAPS:yes   SEASONAL:yes

DISCOUNTS: Ladies $1 off on Monday's. Seniors $1 off Mon-Fri 8am-5pm.

DIRECTIONS:LIE (495) to Exit 53 North (Sunken Meadow Parkway) to exit SM3A.Make a left on Indian Head Rd and proceed 5 traffic lights.

DRIVING RANGE

ISLAND GREEN GOLF CENTER   Range 516 732-4442
Selden, NY   Pro Shop 516 732-4449

BUCKETS: **STATIONS:**76-mats
SMALL $4.00   **LEVELS:**2
MEDIUM $7.50   **COVERED:**yes-38
LARGE $10.00   **HEATED:**yes-38
PRO: James Connors   **LIGHTS:**yes

HOURS: Open 24 hours all season. Winter hours 7am-11pm.

FEATURES\FACILITIES:

PRO SHOP:yes   PRACTICE AREA:yes   DISTANCE MARKERS:yes-greens
SNACK BAR:yes   PUTTING GREEN:yes   LESSONS:yes
MINIATURE GOLF:yes   SAND TRAPS:yes   SEASONAL:no

DISCOUNTS: Early bird special Mon-Fri (open-11am),Sat&Sun (open-8am),$10.00 for 210 balls. Token cards are also available.

DIRECTIONS:LIE (495) to Exit 63.Proceed North on Patchague/Mt. Sinai Rd to Route 25 (Middle Country Rd),make a left and proceed approx. ½ mile to Golf Center on the right.

DRIVING RANGE

NORTH WOODMERE   Range 516 791-8100
North Woodmere, NY

BUCKETS: **STATIONS:**24-mats
SMALL $3.00-30 Balls   **LEVELS:**1
PRO: Tom Berry   **COVERED:**yes-2
                                HEATED:no
                                LIGHTS:yes

HOURS: In season 7am-10pm. Off season 7am-dusk.

FEATURES\FACILITIES:

PRO SHOP:yes   PRACTICE AREA:no   DISTANCE MARKERS:yes-flags
SNACK BAR:no   PUTTING GREEN:yes   LESSONS:yes
MINIATURE GOLF:no   SAND TRAPS:no   SEASONAL:no

DISCOUNTS:4 buckets for $10.

DIRECTIONS: Southern State Parkway to Exit 19 South, Peninsula Blvd. Go South for 6 ½ miles and make a right on Branch Ave. Go 1 mile and follow signs to the range.